10 MINUTES
TO HAPPINESS

SANDI MANN

10 MINUTES TO HAPPINESS

A daily journal that will change your life

ROBINSON

ROBINSON

First published in Great Britain in 2018 by Robinson

13 5 7 9 10 8 6 4 2

A CIP catalogue record for this book is available from the British Library.

ISBN 978-1-47214-123-1

Desgned by Andrew Barron at Thextension
Typeset in The Sans & The Serif
Printed and bound in Great Britain by CPI Group (UK) Ltd, Croydon CRO 4YY

Papers used by Robinson are from well-managed forests and
other responsible sources.

Robinson
An imprint of
Little, Brown Book Group
Carmelite House
50 Victoria Embankment
London EC4Y 0DZ

An Hachette UK Company

www.hachette.co.uk

CONTENTS

....

HOW TO
USE THIS JOURNAL

....

TEN MINUTES TO HAPPINESS IS A THERAPEUTIC SELF-HELP
programme based on a six-step formula designed to lift mood
either on a short-term or long-term basis. It is underpinned by
psychological principles and has been tried and tested among
many of my clients at The MindTraining Clinic in Manchester. And
the best thing of all is that it takes just ten minutes every day!

The programme consists of recording, in this journal, incidents,
events and activities, within six key Domains, at the end of every
day. This is something easily incorporated into most daily routines
and will be unlikely to take more than a few minutes each night.
And, once you get into the habit, you will find that you start
noticing things during the day that you can write in your journal;
in fact, not only will you become more aware of things that you
are doing that can be included in the journal, but you will start
doing things specifically to record in it. This is how *Ten Minutes to
Happiness* can change your life.

Each Domain is carefully chosen and based on sound psychological
theory (which will be explained later). The six Domains are:

1   **Pleasure** things that were enjoyed that day
2   **Positive Strokes** praise received during the day
3   **Lucky Me** good fortune you encountered that day
4   **Achievements** reasons to say, 'Well done me', however small
5   **Gratitude** blessings to be counted
6   **Random Acts of Kindness** kind acts you have performed
    that day

By using this Ten-Minute Programme every day, your life will start to change. Specifically you will:

* Start to enjoy life more – this is because you will begin to look for things to do that give you pleasure in order to have something to write in the journal at the end of the day.

* Feel happier – research shows that noting enjoyment of more things enables people to start to feel happier, too.

* Be better able to lift your mood – when low moods strike, you will be able to read back through your journal and halt the depressive cycle by interfering with emotional memory (more on this later).

* Be better able to accept compliments and recognise and acknowledge the things you have done well that have been appreciated by others. This will boost self-esteem.

* Stop feeling unlucky and get out of the 'why me?' syndrome that can bring us down. By recognising when luck is on our side (and it will be sometimes!), we can use the hard evidence that we are not as unlucky as we might think when we are feeling low.

* Recognise your achievements – many people who feel down are convinced they are 'useless' and good at nothing; this journal will collate the hard evidence that proves otherwise.

* Be more appreciative of what you have rather than focusing on what you don't have.

* Be kinder – you will start performing Random Acts of Kindness in order to complete this Domain in the Journal. As evidence shows, merely recognising and counting acts of kindness can make us feel happier, with this increase in kindness making us happy, too!

How to do the Ten-Minute Programme

You can use this as a weekly or daily journal. Either way, at the end of each day, get into the habit of taking a few minutes to note down anything you can in the boxes. Some boxes will be harder to fill so will not have as many entries as others. For example, positive strokes are, sadly, quite rare – and being lucky doesn't happen too often to most of us either! The point is that both of these do happen at times and this journal will help you note and remember them.

The Notes box allows you to record anything significant about your day or week (e.g. holiday week, or illness, etc.)

Some people prefer to carry the journal around with them and make notes as soon as something happens so they don't forget it; others make notes on their phone and then transfer them at the end of the day into the ten-minute journal. You will soon find the rhythm that works best for you.

This Ten-Minute Programme will provide an ongoing record and evidence of the good things in your life – the reasons to be cheerful. When you feel low, you can look through it and remind yourself of all the reasons to be cheerful that we tend to forget about when we're not feeling so positive. So, keeping this journal will help lift your mood and keep it there!

INTRODUCTION
IT'S SAD TO BE SAD

....

EVERYONE FEELS SAD SOMETIMES. WE ALL FEEL DOWN, or have the 'blues' at times. It's normal. In fact, those down times might even serve a purpose by highlighting the good times. If we didn't have the sad times, we wouldn't appreciate the good times as much. The sad moments provide a contrast against which we can enjoy the happy times.

But some people feel too sad too much of the time. Their down times last too long or sink too low. Or they feel sad without really knowing why – about lots of things, or maybe even everything. These people may or may not suffer from depression; sometimes, they might just describe themselves as feeling a bit 'depressed', without having a clinical diagnosis of depression.

This might describe you. Or perhaps you might have suffered previously or are suffering from clinical depression. You might even be taking antidepressants. If so, you are not alone; according to the World Health Organization, globally, more than 300 million people of all ages suffer from depression.

It doesn't matter who you are or what your label is – this Ten-Minute Programme can still help you. Of course, it is no substitute for medical and professional psychological input and anyone suffering from severe depression should always see their GP.

Whether you feel down a lot or have occasional low moods, or just want to feel happier more often, this programme will help. People who feel sad may suffer from episodes when they are unable to motivate themselves to do much (even to get out of bed), cannot find pleasure in life and feel worthless. There are four main groups of symptoms of low mood:

1   Those to do with feelings: e.g. feeling sad and miserable
2   Physical symptoms: e.g. lack of appetite or sleeping difficulties
3   Thoughts/cognitions: e.g. 'I am worthless', 'no one likes me'
4   Those to do with behaviour: e.g. staying in bed

It might be helpful too for you to note down some of your thoughts and feelings about when you feel down or sad:

1   How do you feel (what other emotions are there, apart from sadness – e.g. guilt, shame, etc.)?

....

....

....

....

....

....

....

2   Where in your body do you feel these emotions (e.g. head, stomach, etc.)?

....

....

....

....

....

....

....

3 What sort of thoughts go through your head
(e.g. I am stupid, I am unlucky, etc.)?

....
....
....
....
....
....
....

4 How do you tend to behave
(e.g. curl up in bed, go for a walk, etc.)?

....
....
....
....
....
....
....

The notes you've just made will begin to show you your
stereotypical pattern of responding to sadness. This may well
change as you start completing the Ten-Minute Programme,
especially if any of your responses are unhelpful.

In general, the thoughts that people have when they are low tend to lead to the other symptoms so it is the thoughts that often control mood. Some common thoughts that people have when they feel low include the following:

Nobody likes me
I always do things wrong
I am unlucky
Nothing ever goes right for me
I am useless

These thoughts are often triggered by incidents or events that happen to us. It might be seeing a social event on Facebook that we were not invited to, getting caught in the rain, doing badly in an exam or making a mistake at work.

EMOTIONAL MEMORY

When people start having these sorts of thoughts they can get locked into a cycle of negative thinking. This is because of 'emotional memory'. Our memories are thought to be stored alongside the emotions that are associated with them. When we experience an emotion, that feeling often triggers other memories that are linked to that same emotion. So when we feel happy, memories of other events that made us happy are triggered. Unfortunately, when we feel down, we remember other events that made us feel bad, too – this is why we start thinking that we are 'always' wrong, or 'never' have friends; our memories of such events are activated when we are sad, so these are all we can think of .[1]

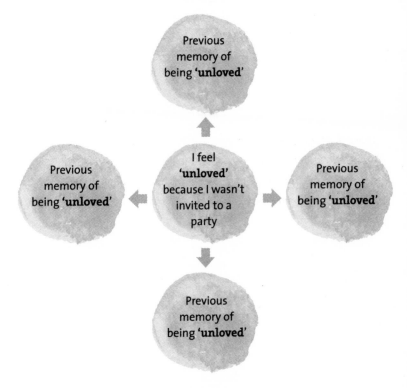

Because so many other sad memories are triggered, our mood gets even lower. Perhaps other emotions become entangled, too – such as feeling unworthy, or even stupid. This triggers other sad memories to be activated which are associated with these new memories – and our mood worsens further. This is how feeling sad can trap us into a negative cycle – and the Ten-Minute Programme can help break that cycle.

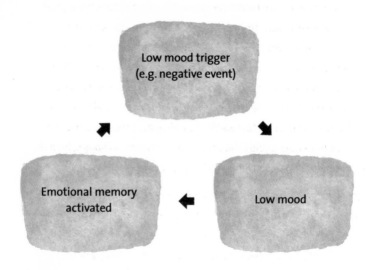

Unhappiness is Unhealthy

You might have heard of the maxim 'think well, be well'. Research suggests there is this link between feeling happy and physical health. In a study of Harvard undergraduates lasting seventy years and published in 2009, researcher George Valliant found a clear link between depression and health problems. Of the men in the study who reported signs of depression at 50 years old, 70 per cent had died or were chronically ill by 65.[2]

This doesn't actually mean that being unhappy will make you ill. It's more likely that being unhappy tends to lead to an unhealthy lifestyle such as comfort eating or lack of exercise and perhaps smoking or drinking more alcohol. Being happy and content may lead to healthier lifestyles with considered food choices and care taken over well-being.

Another study found that people who were unhappy tended to store up longer-term health problems, too. Ohio State sociologists examined data taken from 6,432 participants in the National Longitudinal Survey of Youth (NLYS), which tracks outcomes for people who were between 14 and 22 when it began in 1979. They found that the unhappiest group were more likely to experience depression, sleep problems, 'excessive worry', emotional problems and lower overall mental health. They also reported more back pain and more frequent colds than their happier peers – though, happily, their rate of diagnosed illnesses like cancer was not higher.[3]

Again, it might not be that unhappiness is causing colds and back pain. It might be that unhappiness leads to other symptoms (like the worry, sleep problems, poor diet, etc.) that might lower immunity. It is also possible that when we are unhappy we are more aware of aches and pains than when we are feeling cheerful.

Causes of Unhappiness

What makes people unhappy? This is a question without a definitive answer. Plenty of people have tried to suggest what they think makes people unhappy, but the truth is that there is no one proven cause. It is easier to create a formula for happiness (as I have in this programme) than a formula for unhappiness. Here are some of the likely reasons that people are unhappy:

1. **Lack of meaning in one's life.** Everyone likes to feel they have a purpose and that what they do is of value. If your work has little meaning to you, is boring or otherwise 'pointless', and your day-to-day routine is such that you never feel like you are contributing to society or offering value to the world, it is easy to feel this lack of meaning.

2. **Preoccupation with either the past or the future (instead of the present).** People who obsess about what has been or what might be are not able to enjoy the present. They might worry excessively about things they have done in the past, mistakes they may have made or incidents they regret. Or they may wistfully yearn for times gone by to the extent that they ignore the present. Alternatively, their worries and angst about events that may or may not happen in the future can prevent them focusing on the here and now.

3. **Low self-esteem (comparisons with others).** We all compare ourselves to other people – it is part of the human condition. And nowadays it is even easier to compare ourselves with more people than ever before, thanks to social and mass media. And on Facebook and Instagram, everyone else's lives seem so much better; so much more fun, more exciting and more successful. It is easy to feel inadequate. A 2013 study conducted by University of Michigan psychologist Ethan Kross found a direct correlation between time spent on social media sites and feelings of dissatisfaction, loneliness and isolation.[4] Of course, we forget that people only present carefully edited versions of themselves to the world, and get sucked in to the idea that everyone else is better looking, wealthier, more popular and more successful than we are. See Domain 4 for more on this.

4   Negative thinking. I said earlier that depression and low
mood is often caused by our thoughts. There are certain
habitual patterns of thinking that we can fall into that can
bring us down. For example, only focusing on or noticing
negative things or when things go wrong, and discarding
all those things that go well or that we do well. Negative
thinking can also manifest itself in other ways; some people
are afraid to feel happy in case that happiness 'sets them
up' for disappointment. It is as if by being happy they are
causing something bad to happen to them. This, of course, is
an example of flawed thinking, but is the sort of mindset that
people can find themselves trapped in.

5   Perfectionism. It is good to have high standards but when the
standards we set for ourselves and our world are too extreme,
we are setting ourselves up for failure. Aligned with this is
having unrealistic expectations such as 'life should be fair', or
'bad things should not happen to good people' or even that 'I
should never make mistakes' or 'everyone should like me'.

6   Financial worries. There is no denying that not having enough
money can make us unhappy. Not having enough can make us
anxious and can stop us doing some of the things that would
increase our happiness. But it is worth noting that the converse
isn't always true – money does not in itself make us happy. And,
once we have a certain level of income, having more will not
increase our happiness. Research has shown that very wealthy
people actually suffer from higher rates of depression; a World
Health Organization survey in 2010 interviewed 89,037 people
in 18 countries and found that depression was more likely to hit
those living in high-income countries than poorer ones.[5] One
reason for this might be that acquiring material possessions is

never actually that satisfying; there is always something else to acquire, a new version, the latest model. Being content with less is probably more likely to lead to happiness.

7 **Working too hard.** Not having time to spend doing the things we enjoy and relax us can contribute towards our unhappiness; there is more about this in Domain 1.

8 **Poor social and personal relationships.** Many researchers agree that having good relationships can be one of the most important contributors to being happy. Some of the Domains in this journal will help build these important relationships.

9 **Poor physical health.** Pain, worries about health, unpleasant or invasive medical procedures and so on, are all likely to be causes of unhappiness, especially if this poor health prevents you from doing the things you want to do. However, even people in chronic pain or poor health can be happy, by enjoying things, having good self-esteem and meaningful lives.

Most of these sources of unhappiness are addressed by the Ten-Minute Programme.

You now have an opportunity to think about what would make you happier in life. More money? If so, how much more exactly? A bigger house – why? A better job – what sort of job? Write down your thoughts opposite but really think about them. This will help to focus your mind on what you *think* would make you happy, and what would *really* make a meaningful difference to your state of happiness.

....

....

....

....

....

....

....

The 'Happiest' Countries in the World[6]

1	Denmark	11	Israel
2	Switzerland	12	Austria
3	Iceland	13	United States
4	Norway	14	Costa Rica
5	Finland	15	Puerto Rico
6	Canada	16	Germany
7	Netherlands	17	Brazil
8	New Zealand	18	Belgium
9	Australia	19	Ireland
10	Sweden	20	Luxemburg

The United Kingdom is ranked 23rd out of the 53 countries ranked.

Happiness was measured using a variety of index factors such as: GDP per capita; healthy years of life expectancy; social support (as measured by having someone to count on in times of trouble); trust (as measured by a perceived absence of corruption in government and business); perceived freedom to make life decisions; and generosity (as measured by recent donations).

The data used to rank countries in each report is drawn from the Gallup World Poll, as well as other sources, such as the World Values Survey, in some of the reports. The Gallup World Poll questionnaire measures fourteen areas within its core questions: (1) business and economic; (2) citizen engagement; (3) communications and technology; (4) diversity (social issues); (5) education and families; (6) emotions (well-being); (7) environment and energy; (8) food and shelter; (9) government and politics; (10) law and order (safety); (11) health; (12) religion and ethics; (13) transportation; and (14) work.

THE BENEFITS OF JOURNALING

'Journaling daily is the most potent and powerful keystone habit you can acquire,'[7] wrote Benjamin Hardy in *The Observer* in July 2015.

The Ten Minutes to Happiness programme is based on keeping a journal. It is unlike other journals in that it is Domain-specific and based on research, but the concept of journaling itself has many proven benefits.

Journaling (or diary-writing) is an ancient tradition that dates back to at least the tenth century. The modern diary has its origins in fifteenth-century Italy where diaries were used for accounting. Many famous people throughout history have kept journals, such as presidents and world leaders who have maintained them for posterity. Samuel Pepys' journals recorded life in seventeenth-century England, including historic events like the Great Fire of London in 1666. One of the most famous books in the world is based on a journal: *The Diary of a Young Girl* by Anne Frank.

There is increasing evidence to support the notion that journaling has a positive impact on physical well-being. University of Texas at Austin psychologist James Pennebaker is the author of *Writing to Heal*, which shows how regular journaling strengthens immune cells, and Pennebaker goes so far as to claim that writing about stressful events helps you come to terms with them, thus reducing the impact of those stressors on your physical health. He even suggests that writing about emotions and stress can boost immune functioning in patients with such illnesses as HIV/AIDS, asthma and arthritis. An intensive research review by Smyth, published in 1998 in the *Journal of Consulting and Clinical Psychology* (Vol. 66, No. 1), suggests that writing does indeed make a difference, although the degree of difference depends on the population being studied and the form that writing takes.

Other benefits of daily journaling are thought to be that it 'is a beautiful and powerful facilitator of self-discovery'; it allows you to understand and clear your emotions; and it allows your subconscious mind to work out problems in unique ways, intensifying the learning process and increasing your gratitude.[8]

Additional benefits of journaling are thought to:

* Help you to balance and harmonise events with those of the past and future
* Aid with recall and enable you to reconstruct past events
* Allow you to learn to act as your own counsellor
* Enable perspective when it comes to acknowledging peaks and dips in life
* Help you reconcile and deal with memories of events that are troubling
* Allow a more holistic view of yourself in that it connects various parts of your life

* Show you the patterns and cycles in your life and allow you to track them
* Offer new perspectives

Researchers are only beginning to understand why writing may benefit the immune system. Most agree, however, that the key to writing's effectiveness is in the way people use it to interpret their experiences. To really benefit from writing's healing power, people must use their writing to understand better and learn from their emotions rather than simply to express them[9]. This involves thought and interpretation as well as finding meaning in what is written – something that the Ten-Minute Programme aims to achieve.

I will now introduce each of the six Domains of Happiness. Each Domain includes real case-study examples of journals that clients have completed as part of their Ten-Minute Programme. All text included here is done so with the permission of each client, but all identifying features have been changed.

DOMAIN 1
PLEASURE

....

When we are feeling low, we don't believe that there is much to enjoy in life. In fact, a sure sign of depression is that people don't enjoy the things they used to, don't feel there is anything to look forward to and don't feel that life offers anything pleasurable at all.

But you don't have to be depressed to feel like this. Sometimes, people are so preoccupied with work and getting through the day that they don't find time to do anything enjoyable – and this makes them sad. We all need to have things each day that we enjoy – without pleasure and enjoyment, it is hard to be happy.

This Domain, then, is about seeking pleasure. It is about looking for things that give us pleasure and recognising and acknowledging the joy in our daily lives. Happiness is not just about doing pleasurable things, but about finding the pleasure in things we already do. Many of these things will be about pleasure via our senses and via external experiences.

This Domain is not necessarily therefore about doing amazing things like going on holiday or buying a new car. It is about: (1) finding the pleasure in the mundane, the ordinary, the everyday; and (2) doing more of what we enjoy.

Part of this involves getting used to rating your enjoyment of things. Much of the time, we are so busy with life or so swept up in our own thoughts that we don't realise that we are enjoying something. Stopping and rating our enjoyment on a scale of 0–100 will help us recognise the things that we enjoy, and train us to do more of them (see later for an exercise to do this yourself).

The Rules for this Domain

1 Every single day should include something small that gives pleasure. This could be a great cup of coffee, a relaxing soak in the bath, a walk in the park or a chat with a good friend. Build something into every day. But don't have more than one unhealthy, snack-related 'pleasure' each day (see later).

2 We should seek pleasure in things we do. Got a commute? Sit back and relax . . . and enjoy the ride. Waiting for a bus? Watch the clouds and enjoy nature. Rushing to grab a lunchtime sandwich? Enjoy the fact that you can walk outside in the great outdoors and become more connected with the world.

3 Rate everything remotely pleasurable. You might surprise yourself by noting that you enjoy everyday experiences more than you thought.

4 Start to make arrangements to look forward to as well; make the most of the weekend or plan a short break or a meal out with friends.

5 Write it all down in your journal!

Being in the Now

Part of enjoying life is being in the here and now. It is hard to find pleasure in things if we are worried about what will happen or what has happened. Children are brilliant at being in the here and now – watch toddlers play and they are totally absorbed by whatever they are involved in. When there's sand to play with or dough to shape, they don't sit there worrying about what will happen if the dough dries out or the sand gets wet. They just play and let the next moment take care of itself.

Adults often find it hard to enjoy the here and now. We have so many things to think about, so many worries and concerns. These can stop us enjoying what we have now. We need to learn to stay in the here and now and concentrate on what we feel now, not at some point in the future. We need to be more like kids.

Joy in the Mundane

One of the key aspects to the Pleasure Domain is finding joy in the mundane. We live in a world where we are supposed to capture and share exciting events on social media, so it appears that only those really exceptional parts of our lives are of value. This can lead to high expectations about what we need in order to be happy – an expensive meal, a stunning party, an exotic holiday, for example. Yet there are some people who have learned to rediscover pleasure in far more low-key occurrences. I recently met Leyland Carlson, the Founder of the Dull Men's Club (www.dullmensclub. com), an international web-based group made up of men (and some women) who are proud to enjoy the mundane things in life. Their website celebrates all that is mundane and everyday, with 'dull-lights' (rather than highlights) featuring discussions of park benches, airport carousels and roundabouts. The club began as a real group in New York with 17 members (that was the number of chairs available in the meeting room), but their Facebook page now boasts 3,386 likes (at the time of writing). That's a lot of people who find pleasure in routine, dull, pedestrian, everyday stuff that most people don't even notice.

In my book about boredom (*The Science of Boredom*)[1], I celebrate people who are able to find joy in the mundane rather than the grandiose. In our fast-paced world where nothing seems to sustain our attention for long unless it is 'exciting', there is something charming and, indeed healthy, about taking the time to appreciate the beauty and joy of simple, everyday life. The Dull Men, with their obsessions for lawnmowers and milk bottles and railway tracks, find the pleasure in simple, ordinary things. Perhaps if more of us stopped to appreciate the small stuff, fewer of us would become depressed in the first place.

Look through the following activities that typically are considered to be enjoyable. Rate them from 0–100, where 100 means that you love doing this activity and 0 means you hate it. Then strike through any rated below 30. At the end, you will have a collection of possible enjoyable activities that you can start building into your daily life.

Activity	Rating 0–100
~~Having a long, hot bath~~	20
~~Collecting things~~	20
Playing an instrument	30
~~Playing a team sport~~	20
~~Swimming~~	20
Going for a walk	50
Chatting to a friend	80
Coffee	100
A meal out	80
Coffee and a cake with a friend	90
Going to a party or social event	90
The smell of freshly mown grass	75
Walking in the sunshine	50
Going to a cinema	70

Watching TV	80
Reading a book/magazine	80
Shopping ~ depends	60
Stroking a pet	80
Walking a dog	70
~~Watching children play~~	20
~~Playing with your own children~~	—
Baking/cooking	50
Gardening	70
Being creative (e.g. making jewellery)	60
~~Painting/drawing~~	30
Listening to music	40
~~Writing stories~~	20
~~Looking at old photos~~	20
Taking photos	35
Meeting new people	40
Seeing nice scenery	50
Repairing things	60
Being with the family	50
Sex	80
Singing	30
~~Going to religious activity/service~~	10
~~Feeling the sand between your toes~~	20
Seeing animals ~ not zoo	70
~~Ice-skating/roller-skating~~	10
Travelling	90
Having people round	80

Buying a gift for someone	70
Sightseeing	90
Having beauty treatments	70
Eating	70
Going on social networking sites	60
Surfing the web	70
~~Star-gazing~~	10
Acting	70
Being alone	40
Dancing	75
Day out with the children	—
~~Picnic~~	20
~~Doing crosswords or Sudoku (or similar)~~	10
~~Going to museums or art galleries~~	20
Volunteering in the community	50
~~Doing jigsaws~~	10
~~Having a hot chocolate~~	10
Eating an ice cream	50
Going to a park	70
~~Watching ducks in water~~	20
~~Watching a sunset (or sunrise)~~	20
Seeing the first blossom of spring	60
Standing in the snow	50
Building a snowman	40
Sledging with the kids	—
~~Swinging on a swing or sliding down a slide~~	10
Walking barefoot on the grass or beach	40

The Brain's Pleasure Centres

The part of our brain responsible for feeling pleasure is called the amygdala. This is actually made up of two almond-shaped areas located deep in the temporal lobes of the brain. Most complex vertebrates, including humans, have an amygdala and the area is also linked with memory, emotional learning, aggression and fear. The neurotransmitter dopamine is actually what underlies the feeling of pleasure. Researchers have found that if you ask people to report on how much pleasure they're getting from enjoyable experiences it matches the level of dopamine response.[2] Dopamine is, indeed, commonly associated with the 'pleasure system' of the brain, providing feelings of enjoyment and reinforcement to motivate us to do, or continue doing, certain activities. Certainly, dopamine is released during naturally rewarding experiences such as eating and sex, because these experiences are beneficial for our survival.

'Does the Ten-Minute Programme Allow Me to Eat Chocolate All Day Then?'

Dopamine production feels exciting and stimulating because it is, in evolutionary terms, in our interests for it to be directly related to something we crave. This is because dopamine is associated with those behaviours that are adaptive for us – i.e. designed to help us survive. Eating, of course, has huge evolutionary benefits for us, so our bodies are designed to make us motivated to eat – hence the production of the feel-good dopamine when we eat[3]. And more dopamine is released when we eat sugary or fatty foods, which were likely to increase the chances of survival for our hunger-prone ancestors (although, of course, the opposite is true in the food-rich First World today). In fact, research has shown that junk food affects our dopamine production in much the same way as heroin – albeit with less intensity.[4]

So, we are hard-wired to enjoy eating sugary and fatty foods – and this Domain is all about seeking pleasure, right? Well, not exactly. We have to balance the benefits that short-term pleasure gives us over long-term unhappiness. Eating an excess of foods that will have a poor outcome in terms of our longer-term health means sacrificing long-term happiness for short-term pleasure.

So, the rule is only to seek pleasure from one 'unhealthy' food item each day (as a rough guide; there may be special occasions like holidays and celebrations when this rule is made to be broken). So if you have a lovely crème brûlée hot chocolate (my personal treat) in the morning, enjoy it, savour it, rate it and derive pleasure from it – but give your afternoon Mars Bar a miss. If not, there is a risk of not only poor long-term health, but also weight gain, which can cause greater dissatisfaction with body image and diminished self-esteem, none of which will make you happy.

It is also important not to rely too much on food items for pleasure (or reward) as this risks straying into comfort eating. You will begin to associate pleasure and happiness with eating, which, given the natural pleasure sugary and fatty food gives us, is likely to lead to negative outcomes.

It is therefore essential to find a range of non-food-related activities that give you pleasure, even if you haven't rated them as highly.

Pleasure v Happiness

This Domain is about producing and recognising pleasure in our lives, but we should take care not to become too dependent on 'pleasure' to make us feel happy. This is why this is just one of the six Domains in this programme. If pleasure-seeking was the answer, this book would stop here. But pleasure-seeking on its own is not the key to happiness, and it is important to state that here.

There is a world of difference between happiness and pleasure. Pleasure is a brief, temporary feeling that usually originates from something external. Pleasurable experiences give us momentary feelings of happiness; this is why they are important and why this is a vital part of the Ten-Minute Programme – but this happiness does not last long because it is dependent upon external events and experiences. My morning crème brûlée hot chocolate won't keep me happy all day; in fact, the pleasure from it probably wears off pretty much as soon as I finish the cup. In order to keep feeling happy, we have to keep on having the good experiences – more food, more drugs or alcohol, more money, more sex, more material possessions, etc. As a result, it is easy to become addicted to these external experiences, needing more and more to feel that brief feeling of happiness.[5] Our pursuit of pleasure takes over.

This is not the aim of the Ten-Minute Programme. The aim is to ensure that you have a few things each day that bring pleasure to lift your mood and give you something to look forward to. The aim is not that you spend the entire day in pursuit of pleasure to the exclusion of everything else. In fact, by looking for pleasure in the mundane, the aim is to train your mind to need less and less in order to feel good, not more and more.

The pursuit of pleasure to the exclusion of all else does not bring happiness. We all wish we could stay on holiday for ever, lazing in the sun, drinking cocktails and never doing a stroke of work. But this pleasurable way of life would soon lose its charms since long-term happiness is more tied in with other things that are more meaningful, as discussed in the Introduction. Researchers in the USA found that the kind of happiness derived from seeing your team win or reading a blog post about a cute cat may give us an instant hit of pleasure, but cannot compete with the sort of happiness we glean from doing something purposeful such as helping others[6] (see Domain 6). This is why the 'pleasure principle' of this Domain is only one of six.

Things I Enjoyed Today

When you complete this Domain each day, you might notice that the things that give you pleasure fall into a finite number of themes (and sometimes the things you write will fall into more than one theme):

Theme	Example
Having time and leisure to do things	*The luxury of sitting down and watching a good documentary on TV — something I don't usually have time for.*
Enjoying nature	*I enjoyed a lovely long walk in the warm sunshine this evening. It was so nice to feel the sun on me, to wear shorts, to hear the birds and see the colours of nature.*
Noting enjoyment of small treats	*I really enjoyed an ice-cold Coke on a hot day today.* *A delicious salted caramel ice cream on a hot day.*
Finding pleasure in the little things	*I went on a works away day which was very dull but I really enjoyed the millionaire's shortbread that was provided at break!*

Social stuff	My aunt who lives abroad rang me tonight and it was so nice to speak to her. We had a lovely chat and I realised how lovely it was to catch up.
	Met friends today for coffee and cake. Lovely to see people and feel sociable.
	I went to a party and enjoyed letting my hair down, having a drink or two and just chilling with friends.
	Going out for breakfast with a group of friends to celebrate a birthday.
Family stuff	Today I spent an hour in the evening talking and laughing with my teenage children — something that we rarely have time for. It was so nice to spend quality time with them and to enjoy each other's company.
	Walked the kids to school today — such a treat to take the time to do this. Stopped to collect conkers and play in the park. Lovely, relaxing walk and I enjoyed seeing the kids play.
	My daughter was really kind to another child today which gave me so much pleasure to witness.
Respite	I enjoyed having an afternoon off from work today; I feel like I am always working so it felt so good to just switch off for a while.

I went out for the day with my family and I felt totally engaged with what we were doing — it was as if I left all my cares and concerns behind so it was so nice to have respite from the rest of my life.

The joy in knowing I am off work for ten whole days now for Christmas!

Nostalgia

Spent an hour looking at old photos of when the kids were small. Felt a bit nostalgic but it was pleasurable too.

Experiences

I went on a school trip with my daughter to a zoo; I really enjoyed seeing the children enjoy themselves and seeing my daughter with her little friends.

I went to a school music evening and got so much pleasure out of seeing and hearing my son play the piano.

I went for a bike ride — felt so free and really enjoyed the exercise and the whole experience.

Fish 'n' chip supper on the pier, watching the sea, dodging seagulls — what more could I want?!

Went to the Christmas markets with a friend; really enjoyed the festive atmosphere, the treats we bought and choosing little gifts for family and friends.

Going to the theatre to see a musical — a lovely treat.

Having a lovely meal with my partner in a nice restaurant.

Went to the sales and bought lots of cheap stuff — what a thrill!

I travelled first class for once by train and it was such an enjoyable experience!

Attended a training course which I didn't expect to enjoy but it was surprisingly good fun.

Spent a few hours clothes shopping this morning which I enjoyed.

NB there is no need to worry about themes such as 'Respite' or 'Nostalgia' when you write in this Domain. I have included them here just to help you think about, notice and recognise the range of things that you can include.

DOMAIN 2

POSITIVE STROKES

....

This comes with a warning – Positive Strokes is the hardest Domain to find things to write about in your journal! Positive strokes are the pats on the back or praise that we all need on occasion to build our self-esteem. Admittedly, these are rare for most of us – most of us feel taken for granted much of the time – but if they occur, however minor they seem, you should write them down to give your self-esteem a boost.

When we are feeling down we often don't notice these positive strokes or else dismiss them as unimportant – by noting them in the journal we start to make them more significant. They don't have to be major things; examples here could include a hug from your child or spouse, praise from a friend, positive feedback from your boss . . . even a 'helpful' badge on TripAdvisor or 'likes' on a Facebook post can be positive strokes.

Positive strokes then are those things that make us feel valued, good, loved or needed. The term actually comes from a type of psychological therapy called Transactional Analysis; Eric Berne, the founder of Transactional Analysis, defined a stroke simply as 'a unit of recognition'. They are the equivalent to babies and toddlers of being stroked and hugged to show they are cared for and loved. The point is that we all need them; Berne states, 'These needs are part of our biological and psychological hungers – and these hungers can be satisfied with strokes.'[1] People who feel down often feel undervalued, unloved, unwanted and unneeded, so looking for and collecting positive strokes helps redress this view by proving that you are valued, loved and needed.

The warning that started this Domain cannot be emphasised enough here. Few people receive positive strokes very often! Many people can go days without any significant positive strokes, so don't feel disturbed by not having much to write down here – this does not mean that you are less valued than other people.

Often, we go through our days without even noticing or acknowledging those positive strokes. We might dismiss praise or compliments, for example, minimising their importance. The Ten-Minute Programme helps us to become aware of these strokes, to note them and to appreciate them.

WHY DO WE DISMISS PRAISE OR COMPLIMENTS?

People with low self-esteem are often very uncomfortable with receiving compliments or praise. This is because such Positive Strokes don't fit in with their own view of themselves. We often go through life actively trying to confirm our own hypotheses or views of the world – even when these views are negative about ourselves. This is why we may only notice the times when things go badly for us, since these confirm our view that 'things usually don't turn out well for me'. We dismiss the times when things do go well because they don't fit our scheme (more about this in the Lucky Me Domain). Therefore, if we believe ourselves to be unattractive, stupid, incompetent, etc., we look for incidents that confirm those beliefs. Then we can say to ourselves, 'See, I knew I was stupid! I was right!' This is illustrated nicely by a study that showed students with low self-esteem would prefer to keep a roommate who has a low opinion of them than switch to someone who likes them more.[2]

Types of Positive Strokes

* Strokes can be physical, e.g. a pat on the back, a smile, a hug

* Strokes can be verbal, a quick 'hello', an invitation for a drink, a compliment or praise

* Strokes can be conditional – 'When you bake that chocolate cake I think you're amazing ...'; or unconditional – 'You're amazing!'

* Strokes can be trivial (a like on Twitter or Facebook)

* Strokes can also be very significant – a letter of thanks and appreciation from a client

Whatever they are, they should be acknowledged, recognised and noted in this Domain in the journal.

If someone tries to challenge our belief (that we are stupid, attractive, incompetent, etc.), we feel a dissonance between what we feel to be true (our own negative belief) and what has been said. This dissonance, or disconnect, makes us uncomfortable and we can reduce the dissonance by either changing our belief or finding reason to negate the compliment – e.g. by dismissing the compliment as unimportant or originating from someone who doesn't know anything, or by assuming they are simply wrong, just being kind or even lying. This allows us to retain our self-belief.

How People Negate Positive Strokes When They Are Sad

Verbal denial instead of graciously accepting the compliment or praise, people might openly disagree with a compliment and even argue with the giver of the compliment. For example, 'This old thing . . . it makes me look fat!' or 'What do you mean I did the presentation well? I lost my place twice and stuttered all the way through it!'

Non-verbal denial here, you might not openly disagree with the giver of the compliment, but might smile politely and say thank you. But inside, you are thinking, 'No way . . . this person doesn't know what they are talking about.' You don't want to get into a whole cycle of them trying to persuade you (after all, they never will) so this is the easiest route for you.

Focusing on the negative here, you can only see the things that were not so good and ignore the rest. So, if someone compliments your lovely dinner party efforts, you will dismiss the compliment because, although all went really well, you focus on the fact that there was a bit of a delay while the main course was cooking. The one negative outshines all the positives.

Redirection because compliments and praise make you so uncomfortable, you redirect attention to your negatives. So, if someone admires your new top, you will immediately remind yourself that you are a bit overweight so it doesn't really matter if your top is nice or not.

Reversing it here, you simple deflect the compliment to the other person; if they say you are clever, you say, 'Oh no, I am not . . . you are the clever one!' Or if someone says you look nice, you immediately dismiss that by saying, 'Never mind me, you look amazing!'

It will be helpful now for you to think a little more closely about how you handle compliments and positive strokes. Answer the following questions to gain more insight into your natural reactions:

How would you typically react to the following compliments?

1   Love your outfit!

....

....

....

....

....

....

2   Great job delivering that presentation!

....

....

....

....

....

....

3   You are so kind!

....

....

....

....

....

....

4 What a great friend you are!

....
....
....
....
....
....

What the Ten-Minute Programme does with this Domain is help change the self-belief instead. By acknowledging and noting the positive stroke, we are forced to confront the idea that maybe our self-belief was inaccurate.

FINDING POSITIVE STROKES

Of course, the whole point about positive strokes is that you can't ask for them. Asking for praise or a compliment, or even a hug, negates much of its benefit. But you can put yourself in situations where you might be more likely to get them, and you can make a point of looking for and noticing them when they do arrive.

I once had a client, a student, with low self-esteem, who was sure that no one liked her. Her evidence for this was that people didn't ask her to join them for social events and, in fact, rarely spoke to her. This all sounded like pretty damning evidence of her being unlikeable ... until I probed further. I discovered that she was so sure of her social rejection that she avoided social contact. She didn't speak to anyone, kept her head down and avoided eye contact. Unsurprisingly, few people did speak to her or invite her to things. This then confirmed her suspicions that she was unlikeable.

As an experiment, I encouraged her to change her behaviour and put herself in situations where the positive strokes might flow more freely. She started to look people in the eye at college, to smile at them and even to exchange the odd comment about a lecture or the weather. To her amazement, people tended to smile back at her and to engage her in small talk. She noted these as positive strokes in her journal. After more of this casual contact, she was even asked to join a crowd for a coffee after a lecture – bingo! A powerful positive stroke: 'They must like me after all!' But the whole point is that when she hid away, she was not allowing herself to be in a position to receive strokes.

Another way to chalk up those positive strokes is to give them out. The more we give, the more we'll probably receive. So when my client gave out smiles, she received smiles in return. Make someone else feel good and they might make you feel good, too – if not straight away, then on another occasion.

BEWARE OF BEING TOO NEEDY

The caveat that started this Domain has another angle to it. Being too reliant on positive strokes for your self-esteem can be unhealthy, too, as you can become quite needy, desperately seeking that affirmation that you are liked and valued. This is why it is vital not to seek praise, compliments or attention actively as this can be quite addictive. You might know people (or you may be that person) who constantly posts needy comments on Facebook such as 'feeling sad', or those attention-seeking statements such as 'some friends are really two-faced', etc. These are posts that beg for attention and demand positive strokes. They are yearnings for people to reassure the poster that they are loved, a good friend, cared for, etc. The poster checks and rechecks their feed constantly to see how many likes they have chalked up; they might get the positive strokes they yearn for, but they are solicited and, if this is done repeatedly, it will lead to gradually diminishing returns; i.e. fewer and fewer people will rush to offer reassurance, which means that the poster feels less and less loved and thus more and more in need of positive strokes.

There is no doubt that positive strokes can feel good and even give us a buzz, so it is not surprising that some people crave them. If this Domain in your journal is full to bursting, you may question whether you are addicted to positive strokes and seeking them out in an unhealthy way.

Facebook Feedback and Insecurity

A study carried out by researchers at Union College in Schenectady, New York, and published in the journal *Personality and Individual Differences* in 2015,[3] suggested that people who are generally insecure in their relationships are more actively engaged on the social media site – frequently posting on walls, commenting, updating their status or 'liking' something – in the hope of getting attention. Such people, said the researchers, were higher in 'attachment anxiety' and worry that other people don't like them as much as they want to be liked, and are also chronically concerned about rejection and abandonment. Their feelings of self-worth are almost totally reliant on feedback on their posts; when they receive a lot of likes and comments they feel good, but less positive attention makes them feel unworthy, unloved and insecure.

If this is you, take note and consider getting professional input to help you work on your insecurity.

Examples of Positive Strokes

Remember that these are relatively rare. In the examples that follow, my clients have recognised and acknowledged the positive strokes rather than actively seeking them out.

Themes	Examples
Work	A client gave me positive feedback and offered to write a review for me.
	Got a repeat order from a client who was obviously happy with my work.
	Got two customers on recommendation so I must be doing something right.
	Chosen to go on a leadership training course at work which made me feel that my qualities have been recognised.
Social	Invited to two parties this week.
	Being told that I have been a really good friend to someone and they couldn't have managed without me.
Social media	Got lots of 'likes' on my Facebook post — this is reassuring as I am never sure if people bother to read my posts. I feel that they must care about me a little bit.
	Got a 'helpful' vote on my TripAdvisor review — I know this is a very minor positive stroke but it does show that someone appreciates my efforts.

	Over 100 birthday wishes on Facebook – I know it is easy to hit 'happy birthday' but still it makes me feel valued that so many people bothered.
Personal qualities, taste or choices	Someone admired my new bag this week and asked where I got it from. Made me feel good that I had chosen well.
	A friend commented that my hair was nice; I felt good that I looked OK.

DOMAIN 3
LUCKY ME
....

One of the surest signs of lowered mood is being convinced that things never go right. Sad or depressed people believe this because they are more likely to notice the occasions when things go wrong and discount or dismiss the times when they have been lucky (this is all to do with emotional memory as outlined in the Introduction, where we associate memories with feelings). Thus, we might really believe that it always rains when we have an important meeting, or that the trains are always late for us or that we will never win that job. By noting the times when good things happen – when the sun shines, when luck was on our side – we collect the evidence to counteract those times when we are feeling down and unlucky. This should halt that depressive 'why me?' cycle.

ARE YOU LUCKY OR UNLUCKY?

Whenever I work with sad or depressed clients they seem to be united by a common complaint – 'Nothing ever goes well for me, I am always unlucky.' Is this actually true? Are some people more lucky than others?

Have a think about your own experiences, and tick the box of the category over the page that best describes you:

How lucky do you think you are compared to other people?

1 Much luckier than most ☐

2 A bit luckier than most ☐

3 About the same as others ☐

4 A bit unluckier than others ☐

5 Much unluckier than others ☐

If you scored 4 or 5, you really need this chapter, and this Domain is going to be very important to help you challenge your beliefs. But even if you scored 1–3, you should still take this Domain seriously; often, people's estimates of how lucky they are vary according to their most recent experiences. So, if you score 1–3 now, it might easily become 4 or 5 in a few weeks. This Domain of the journal will help ensure that the 1–3 scores stay stable.

Psychologists such as Richard Wiseman (author of *The Luck Factor*) have been researching luck for decades and are fascinated by the idea that some people seem to live such a charmed life while others seem perpetually unlucky. Yet they have discovered that so-called 'lucky' people are no luckier than anyone else. The difference is that these people notice the good things that happen to them by chance more than they notice the bad things (a process called selective perception). Both lucky and unlucky people may win a coin toss 50 per cent of the time, but the lucky person will be delighted that they won half the time while the unlucky person will lament that they lost half the time. It is the classic glass half empty or half full scenario.

Thus, the 'unlucky' person notices every time their luck fails and sees it as further evidence of proof that they are unlucky. And, by the very nature of chance, they will be right about half the time! Their hypothesis about themselves will be 'proven' and, indeed, becomes self-fulfilling, as they dismiss any times when their luck is in as this does not fit with their schema about themselves (see more on the idea of a 'schema' later in this Domain). The 'lucky' person is either more realistic in their observations ('Ah well, you win some, you lose some . . .') or even optimistic ('It's usually sunny when I go on holiday!') – they notice the lucky things that happen to them more than the unlucky.

This Domain of the Ten-Minute Programme is aimed at helping you become that 'lucky' person, simply by noting and collecting all the times your luck is in.

THE HABITS OF LUCKY PEOPLE

'Lucky' people do more than just notice the times Lady Luck smiles down on them. They actually act and behave differently from 'unlucky' people. This is why considering yourself unlucky can become part of a self-fulfilling prophecy. This is what 'lucky' people do to help make themselves so lucky:

1 They are open-minded – this means being open to new experiences and possibilities. Rather than have a rigid approach to life and how things should be done, they can be flexible so that when things go wrong, they can simply adapt their plans rather than wallow in the disaster. 'Lucky' people know that there is more than one way to reach their goal and that there will be twists and turns along the way – many of which will turn out to offer better opportunities than the original route. An 'unlucky' person might reject a date as being unsuitable and lament the waste of an evening; the lucky person might reject the date as a suitor but consider them as a friend, business contact or even potential suitor for someone else they know.

Lucky people are also more open-minded in the way they view the world; they are more curious and examine things from all angles. Richard Wiseman conducted an intriguing study in which he recruited people who believed they were lucky and also people who believed the opposite. He gave both groups a booklet and asked them to count how many photos were in the booklet. The lucky group came up with their answer far quicker than the second group. This wasn't because they were faster counters, but because, on the inside page, printed in large letters, was the answer! The lucky people tended to be more observant and thus more likely to notice the answer while the unlucky ones were more likely to miss it.[1]

The lack of observation shown by the unlucky people might be because unlucky people tend to be more anxious – and anxiety can make us less likely to notice things. In an experiment, people were shown a computer screen on which they had to spot large dots. It was an easy task, until the stakes were raised (and thus the level of anxiety) by offering financial incentives for finding the dots. Suddenly, it became harder to find the dots.[2] Similarly, when we are anxious, we are too focused on our problems to notice the world around us – and thus we may miss opportunities.

2 They look for opportunities – 'lucky' people talk to strangers, they network, they investigate things. They are always on the lookout for something or someone that might be useful to them. It is not luck that sees them meet exactly the right person to help back their new venture, or discover just the product they need to meet their needs – it is an active search for opportunity.

Wiseman conducted another experiment with people who consider themselves to be lucky and those who consider themselves unlucky. He left money on the ground and also planted a useful business contact in a coffee shop they frequented. The 'lucky' people noticed the money and struck up a potentially useful conversation with the businessman, while the 'unlucky' ones tended to do neither.[3]

3 They try to see the positive when things go wrong – bad things happen to lucky people, too. The difference is that these people try to turn an unlucky break into a lucky one. They search for the silver lining: 'OK, this didn't go as planned, but maybe something good can come out of what did happen.' This always reminds me of the inventor of the Post-it notes. He was trying to create an adhesive but the one he came up with was a disaster – it was far too lacking in stickiness. Luckily, he saw the potential in a non-permanent glue and the rest is history.

4 They will take risks – getting a lucky break sometimes involves taking a bit of a risk. Staying at home in a safe, secure environment will reduce the chance of something going wrong, but will also reduce the chance of something going right. I always stayed in a particular hotel when on my frequent business trips to York; I knew where I was with it, I felt relaxed and comfortable there. On one trip, though, the hotel was full and I was very perturbed. Forced to stay elsewhere, I found an even better hotel – and it was cheaper, too! Perhaps if I had been more adventurous to start with, I might have been luckier earlier.

Of course, with risk comes the possibility of failure, too. My second-choice hotel might have been a rat-infested dump. That's the chance you take – sometimes you will win and sometimes you will lose. Being afraid of losing means you won't expose yourself to the chance of winning either.

LUCKY CHARMS – WHO NEEDS THEM?

Even with all the habits of a lucky person, good fortune is still not something that can ever come entirely through merit and hard graft. This might go some way to explaining why some people have 'lucky charms' or objects that they believe can bring about good fortune. These usually come about when something lucky happens to someone; almost unable to believe their good fortune, they cast around looking for the source of their luck. Their gaze might alight on some seemingly random object like a necklace they are wearing or even lucky pants. Perhaps they will remember another occasion when they were lucky (which happens due to emotional memory, as discussed in the Introduction) and realise that they also had that object with them then! Ah-ha! The luck must be entirely due to that particular scarf . . . or that pen . . . or that pair of shoes . . . and so on!

Popular Good-Luck Charms

Whether it's a charm, amulet or statue, humans have been using good-luck charms for thousands of years for anything from bringing financial success to warding off evil. Here are some of the more common ones:

Four-leaf clover – the four-leaf clover is an ancient Irish symbol of luck. The Celts believed that a four-leaf clover could help them see fairies and avoid 'fae' (fairy) mischief, a common source of bad luck.

Lucky horseshoe – some people say that horseshoes are lucky because they were traditionally made of iron, which kept away mischievous fairies.

Lucky number 7 – the ancient Greeks called 7 'the perfect number', the sum of 3 (triangle) and 4 (square), which are perfect forms.

Lucky rabbit-foot charm – the original legend says that the left hind foot of a rabbit that is captured in a cemetery at night can ward off evil magic.

Lucky coin or penny – as encapsulated by the saying 'see a penny, pick it up and all day long you'll have good luck'.

The funny thing is that believing in a lucky charm can actually appear to make you luckier. Imagine a football player heading for an important match or a student for a vital exam. They feel around in their pocket for their lucky charm. Imagine their distress if they can't find it! They'll become agitated, believing that they won't perform well without it. And, because they are so distracted and distressed, they do indeed perform badly – a fact they ascribe not to their distress, but to the absence of their charm. On the other hand, if they find their charm, they will be more relaxed and confident, which will invariably lead to a better performance. The charm acts in the same way as a security blanket that small children like to carry around with them. As Stuart Vyse, psychologist and author of *Believing in Magic: The Psychology of Superstition*, points out, 'Lucky charms create an illusion of control for the person who believes in them.'[4]

This is indeed borne out by the research. In a 2010 study involving golf, researchers told half the participants that the golf ball they were using was lucky. Those who thought they were putting with a lucky ball were better at putting than the other participants.[5] In another study, a group of participants who had lucky charms were recruited for a series of memory tasks. Half of them were not permitted to keep their charms with them. Guess who performed better? Yes, the participants who had their lucky charms with them.[6]

The Golem Effect and the Pygmalion Effect

The Golem Effect shows that lower expectations lead to poorer performance by an individual.

On the other hand, the Pygmalion Effect shows that if you instil high expectations within yourself, your future performance will be significantly increased. Both these are self-fulfilling prophecies, and show how lucky charms can impact us.

Having a lucky charm then brings confidence and is fairly low cost. The problem arises if the charm goes missing, of course. It is far better to rely on your own inner strength than a charm as it is harder to mislay! Believing that you are lucky can be just as beneficial as believing in a lucky charm; research has shown that people who believe they are lucky will try harder and be more persistent at challenging activities than people who don't feel they are lucky.[7] And, of course, the more they persist, the more likely they are to succeed – which reinforces their view that they are lucky!

If I Believe I Am Lucky, Will I Be More Likely to Win the Lottery?

Sadly, belief in one's own luck can only get us so far. That positive self-belief can make us take on new challenges and try harder at them and thus feel luckier in life, but when it comes to genuine matters of luck, 'lucky' people are actually no luckier than 'unlucky' ones. Richard Wiseman, the psychologist often associated with luck research, recruited 700 people who were planning to buy lottery tickets. He asked them to complete a self-report questionnaire that measures whether people consider themselves to be lucky or unlucky. There was no difference in winnings between those who rated themselves lucky and those who didn't (although the lucky people felt more confident about winning).[8]

The Benefits of Feeling Lucky

People who rate themselves as lucky have been found to feel more satisfied with life on a range of measures such as family life, personal life, financial situation, health and career.[9]

That is why this Domain is included in the Ten-Minute Programme. Once you start noting and acknowledging when lucky things happen, your mood will start to lift and should, over time, be maintained.

Good Fortune

There is sometimes some overlap between this Domain and 'Gratitude' (Domain 5). Sometimes lucky occurrences are things to be grateful for. But the things that go in the 'Lucky Me' section should be those things that happen to you by the pure good fortune of Lady Luck, whereas the 'Gratitude' section is more acknowledging those things that can't really be ascribed to luck. For example, feeling grateful to have a good friend or a loving family is not really down to pure good luck, so it is better placed in the 'Gratitude' Domain. However, if you are unsure, it doesn't really matter which Domain you place things in – just don't put the same thing in two Domains!

Here are some examples of good fortune:

Having a flexible job that allows me to choose the hours I work; I feel lucky because most of my friends don't have this sort of job.

I was able to grab some cheap train tickets to London for when I needed to go.

I was lucky with the weather today with our planned barbecue; the day before and after it rained, but today was gloriously sunny!

Our holiday was this week and not last — this week, although the weather wasn't perfect, it was a whole lot better than last week when it rained all week!

Although I got to the station late for my train, the train arrived late so I made it!

I found a lovely pair of boots in the sales that were my size!

The theatre allowed me to swap my tickets when I discovered that I could no longer attend on the evening I had booked.

Lucky to find a parking space today near a training event I was attending — only managed that because someone was leaving just as I was getting desperate and thought I would be late.

I was so lucky to find the perfect outfit for a wedding I am attending.

I won a prize today in a raffle! £50 — how lucky am I??

My favourite chocolates were reduced just in time for me to snap them up for my birthday treat to myself!

I booked a random hotel for my work training, not entirely sure where it was or how far in relation to the training event, but I was delighted to discover it was right opposite the training centre. Pure good luck!

Lucky that I took a different route home from work tonight — there was an accident on my normal route and it would have taken me hours to get back.

ACHIEVEMENTS

. . . .

This Domain is all about having a space to note and record
achievements – however small and insignificant they might
seem. People with low mood tend to believe that they are no
good at anything or that they can't achieve much. Even when
they do achieve something, they discount it – 'It was nothing …
anyone could have done that …', etc. Writing down any and every
tiny accomplishment enables people to build up a record of what
they can do or have managed to accomplish during the day.
Accomplishments can be anything from managing to go for a
short walk to cooking a meal from scratch or finishing a tax return.

But I Never Have Any Great Achievements!

Remember that this Domain is not about recording what you are
good at as such, but more about noting what you have managed
to accomplish in a day. It is more about ticking off your 'to-do' list
than it is about getting an A* in A-level Maths – although if you do
get that, you should certainly note that here!

Children are often told that everyone is good at something.
Parents spend time nurturing their talents by enrolling them in
music lessons, karate club or athletics, all aimed at developing and
spotting the child's talent, for it is assumed that everyone has one.

But we are selling our kids a bit of a lie. Not everyone has a talent
or something that they excel at. Most people are just mediocre at
most things – but that should be OK, too. In fact, being OK at lots
of things might be more useful than excelling at one thing – it's

great to have been a star trumpet player at school but unless you currently play in an orchestra, the chances are you probably rarely pick up a brass instrument these days.

So, in this Domain we are not expecting greatness. The idea is to note and record personal achievements, not evidence of talented mastery. For example, a person watching their weight might consider resisting a cream cake as an achievement, while a busy mum juggling kids and work might consider every day her kids get to school on time as an achievement.

According to the business magazine *Forbes*, the one thing that successful business people do is to 'document their wins' each day.[1] This, they claim, brings a number of work-related benefits but, from a personal point of view, it acknowledges what makes you great; unless you are brimming with self-confidence, you might not think you are very great at all. This might be due to poor self-esteem, which we will explore later in this Domain. But it could also be because you are not noticing the things you have done well or achieved. Like the things that are the result of luck in the last Domain, this is about selective perception; we probably notice all the things we do wrong, but not what we do right. That's life – our workplaces and family probably only really notice our failings but not our successes; our kids will complain bitterly if dinner isn't on the table at 6.00pm but rarely congratulate you when it is.

Taking a moment for self-congratulation is an important confidence-booster – 'Look what I have managed to do …' – especially when things don't go right. Perhaps you made a mistake at work today, but you can look back at your journal and see all the times you didn't make mistakes documented in this Domain.

The Zeigarnik Effect

This is our mind's tendency to get fixated on unfinished tasks and forget those we've completed. It is named after psychologist Bluma Zeigarnik who, in 1927, first studied the phenomenon after her professor, well-known psychologist Kurt Lewin, noticed that a waiter had better recollections of orders that hadn't yet been paid. However, after the completion of the task – after everyone had paid – he was unable to remember any more details of the orders.

Writing down accomplished tasks in your journal helps overcome this effect.

THE BENEFITS OF THE 'DID-DO' LIST

This Domain is really the opposite of a to-do list, which is all about keeping records of what you have yet to accomplish. Instead, it builds on the success of what many researchers are calling 'did-do' lists, which encourage you to feel good about what's been achieved rather than feeling anxious about what you still need to do. The idea first seems to have originated in blogs for new mums who felt frustrated that their time just seemed to disappear without appearing to have much to show for it. Creating the 'I did it' lists gave a sense of accomplishment and helped boost confidence.

So to help you to build some evidence of all your accomplishments, write a 'did-do' list of all the things you have done over the past week. Include everything that you might normally put on a to-do list:

My 'Did-Do' List

....

....

....

....

....

....

....

....

....

....

How Low Self-Esteem Can Sabotage Us

Many people have difficulties at first with this Domain because they are sabotaged by low self-esteem. Self-esteem refers to how we feel about ourselves – the value or worth that we feel we have. Someone with high self-esteem will like themselves, be aware of what they are good at and accepting of the things they are less good at. Someone with low self-esteem, on the other hand, does not like themselves as much, believes that they are good at very few things and tends to over-focus on the things that they are bad at. Self-esteem differs slightly from self-confidence which refers more to our ability to do something rather than our overall sense of self-worth. For example, I have poor self-confidence in my ability to sing in tune (sadly!), but it doesn't affect my self-esteem because I don't believe my lack of musical ability makes me a 'rubbish' or unworthy person – just a poor singer.

In the following section, put a cross against any of the symptoms that relate to you:

How many of these symptoms of low self-esteem do you experience?

* Making unfavourable comparisons with other people ☐

* Inability or difficulty in acknowledging positive qualities/ achievements ☐

* Distorted thinking, e.g. believing that I must be perfect, I must not make mistakes, I must be good company, etc. ☐

* Unrealistic understanding of how much other people scrutinise you ☐

* Over-concern with other people's judgements ☐

* Inability to let go of 'failures' ☐

* Blaming yourself for things going wrong ☐

Happiness and self-esteem are intimately linked. There is an abundance of research suggesting that those who are happy also tend to feel good about themselves and those who lack self-worth are generally unhappy. In a University of Michigan study of well-being in America, the best predictor of general life satisfaction was not satisfaction with family life, friendships, or income, but satisfaction with self.[2]

Boost Self-Esteem by Noting Accomplishments

As Thomas Carlyle wrote, 'Nothing builds self-esteem and self-confidence like accomplishment.'

Every single little thing you accomplish in your day, whether it be getting the ironing done or landing your dream job, helps boost your self-esteem. Each accomplishment sends a message to your brain that you are capable, worthy, useful and that you add value. These positive messages motivate you to do more and achieve more and, most importantly, make yourself feel good about yourself. It is much harder to feel that you are a useless waste of space when your journal is brimming with accomplishments.[3]

You could even build on your self-esteem further by setting yourself challenges over and beyond your daily routine. Perhaps take up a hobby, take a class, learn something new, try a new recipe, ring an old friend, stretch beyond your comfort zone ... anything that pushes you that little bit. Not only will this give you something to write in your journal beyond the mundane, but it will also meet some of the objectives of the previous Domain, too.

Start to think about what challenges you could set for yourself now. What new hobbies or interests could you develop? The space below is for you to start to build that list:

Challenges, Hobbies or Interests I Will Try

....

....

....

....

....

....

....

....

....

....

....

....

One of the great things about writing your personal accomplishments in this Domain is that it reduces the element of social comparison. Humans are inherently social creatures and we compare ourselves to other people all the time. This, unless we are super-confident, is very damaging to our self-esteem, since there will always be someone who is cleverer, more attractive, wealthier, etc., than we are. In the age of social media where we can compare ourselves not just with our immediate neighbours and friends (who are likely to be fairly similar in terms of socio-economic class) but with anyone and everyone in the entire world, this can cause extra difficulties. We are spending more and more time seeing the edited highlights of the rich and famous as well as those acquaintances who seem to have the most exciting lives compared to ours. Their collective accomplishments seem incredible compared to ours – it is no wonder we feel inadequate.

The Boost of Small Wins

Often when people start this Ten-Minute Programme, they find this Domain quite difficult because they believe, mistakenly, that the things they're being encouraged to record are insignificant – too trivial to note. Yet frequent small wins can give us as much of a boost as the rare big wins. If we relied on the really big achievements to make us feel good, few of us would ever get that win. For most of us, it is those small accomplishments, and the pride and satisfaction of achieving them, that boost our morale and keep us motivated – not the big ones.

→

A report in *Harvard Business Review* pointed out that it is reaching the 'minor milestones' that helps us keep focused, self-confident and motivated to keep going.[4] Indeed, a number of studies have found that major life events seldom have lasting effects on subjective well-being. For instance, winning the lottery does not usually make people happy in the long term, although it certainly gives a short-term boost of euphoria. But regular minor boosts from ordinary activities can have a cumulative and lasting effect.[5] This is because each achievement or 'small win' gives us a hit of dopamine; that feel-good chemical in our brain. If we have lots of those frequently, we ensure a regular top-up of dopamine, which is better for our mental health than larger amounts very infrequently.

In his book *Feeling Good*, Dr David Burns discusses how important it is to keep track of, reflect on and celebrate not just our major achievements, but also our seemingly minor ones. This means breaking down goals into smaller, more manageable objectives to get those morale-boosting small wins. For example, if your goal is to get that dream job, break that goal down into more manageable small wins such as creating a CV, finding vacancies, applying for jobs, attending suitable courses, etc.

The Ten-Minute Programme requires you to recognise and note your own accomplishments only. These are not relative to anyone else's. You are not asked to post them on Facebook alongside someone else's boast of having climbed Everest. In fact, the whole point of this Domain is that these are personal, private notes. They rely on self-congratulation, not the recognition of others (which is covered in the 'Positive Strokes' Domain). When we can learn to recognise and applaud our own achievements, without being reliant on other people for praise, our self-esteem is strengthened.

ACHIEVEMENTS

Achievements can generally be grouped into rough themes. Many of the items that follow might seem quite small or insignificant when reading them here, but to the authors, they were worthy of being classed as an achievement. Achievements are thus very personal – and also they really don't need to be major things to be noted and acknowledged.

Theme	Example
Getting tasks done	I managed to get a lot of work done today.
	Conquered that huge pile of ironing at last.
	Finally sent off my tax return.
	Managed to organise my child's birthday party, present wrapping, baking, etc. – all went smoothly.
	I managed to make a start on a project I have been putting off for so long – feels good to have finally started it.

Did a much-needed clear-out of the garage at last.

Sorted out all my photos — a job I have been wanting to do for ages.

Had so much to do to clear my desk before going on holiday but I managed it.

Booked tickets for my upcoming work trip and made all the arrangements without leaving it until the last minute as I usually do.

Sold a load of old toys at a car boot sale and made £200.

Found a product I have been looking for for a long time.

Healthy diet	Had a really healthy diet day.

Lost 2 lbs this week.* |
| Exercise | Joined a gym.

Walked 10 miles today.

Made myself go to a spinning class I have been thinking about for a while — and I enjoyed it!

Went swimming twice this week. |

Stretched comfort zone	Pushed myself out of my comfort zone and travelled to a new place that I have always been a bit wary of getting to.
	I worked out how to use a new IT system at work and have started to use it.
	Used contactless payment for Tube in London — something which I haven't done before but felt I should do.
	I stood up for myself when someone at work suggested I wasn't pulling my weight.
	Started an evening course learning Spanish — something I always wanted to do.
Did something well	I passed a course I attended at work.
	I felt really tired but I managed to get through the day.
	I felt that my presentation at work went very well and that all my hard work paid off.
	Grouted the bathroom — not a task I have ever done before but I decided to just give it a go (and it looks OK!).
	I made good choices today.

Overcame barriers	Managed to book flights and hotel myself even though I find the whole process stressful.
	I was very anxious about things today but managed to put those worries aside to enjoy a day out with my family.
	I felt depression descending today — everything felt so awful. But I managed to shake it off and I feel OK now.
	Nervous about flying but managed to go on holiday and enjoyed it.
	Coped well with a very hectic week — usually I would get really stressed about this.
	Resisted the temptation to buy a load of half-price Easter eggs which I really don't need!

* This is an achievement for someone aiming to lose weight but I don't want to imply here that this would be an achievement for everyone or that weight loss is something we should all be aiming for!

DOMAIN 5
GRATITUDE
. . . .

It is easy to get stuck in a negative cycle of worries, problems, bad luck and misfortune. Maybe things really are not going well for you – but there are always things to be grateful for. Perhaps you have enough food to eat (or even enough teeth to eat it with), or healthy children or a safe place to live. Looking for things to be grateful for makes us appreciate life more and thus feel happier and more content. You are encouraged to put a different thought down here each time – some will be general (e.g. grateful to be able to go for a walk) and others more topical (e.g. grateful that my test results were good):

What Do I Feel Grateful for Right Now?

....

....

....

....

....

....

....

....

....

....

....

....

....

Research consistently shows the value of being grateful. In fact, there are a range of proven benefits to being grateful:

1 Gratitude improves physical health – researchers in 2012 conducted a study on adults, which showed that a weekly gratitude journal was beneficial not only in making them feel more optimistic, but it also produced a reduction in physical ailments, such as aches and pains.[1] This might be because those people who were more grateful tended to exercise more often and were more likely to attend regular check-ups, which may well contribute to their longevity. Other studies have shown a raft of health benefits associated with being grateful; one study in 2003 of people keeping a gratitude journal showed that they experienced:[2]

* 10 per cent less pain
* 16 per cent fewer physical symptoms
* 19 per cent more time exercising
* 8 per cent more sleep (and 25 per cent increased sleep quality)

Again, the key to all these health benefits may be exercise since that alone could well be responsible for fewer symptoms and more sleep, but why do grateful people exercise more? It could be that being grateful makes us more appreciative of what we have – and more determined to keep those benefits. We might be more interested in looking after ourselves because we are enjoying life more and want to continue to do so.

Another study in 2007 found that people with hypertension who were asked to count their blessings just once a week showed a significant reduction in systolic blood pressure.[3] Again, this might be due to the exercise effect, or it might be due to the relaxing effect that gratitude has on our bodies and mind.

2 Gratitude improves psychological health – one study by American researchers asked young adults to keep a daily journal of either things they were grateful for or things that annoyed them. Those assigned to keep gratitude journals showed greater increases in determination, attention, enthusiasm and energy compared to the other groups.[4] Another study in 2012 did not involve gratitude diaries but instead examined how much gratitude people tended to show (rather than record) in their daily lives. They found that higher levels of gratitude were associated with better sleep (see later), and with lower anxiety and depression.[5] And, Robert Emmons, a leading gratitude researcher, confirms that gratitude effectively increases happiness and reduces depression.[6]

3 Showing gratitude helps make friends – according to a 2014 study published in *Emotion*, thanking a new acquaintance makes people more likely to seek an ongoing relationship with them and vice versa; friendships can be developed by expressing thanks and gratitude towards someone.[7] In addition, gratitude makes us more trusting, more social and more appreciative, all of which makes people want to be around us more. This probably is one of the points of gratitude as an emotion; all emotions evolved for a reason and showing gratitude towards someone indicates a recognition of reciprocity; if I am grateful to you I am likely to want to repay that debt. These were the wheels that probably kept social bonds going in our evolutionary past.

4 Being grateful makes us kinder – grateful people are more likely to behave in a prosocial manner, even when others behave less kindly, according to a 2012 study by the University of Kentucky. Study participants who ranked higher on gratitude scales were less likely to retaliate against others, even when given negative feedback.[8]

5 Grateful people sleep better – expressing your appreciation and gratitude in a journal like this one improves sleep, according to a 2011 study published in *Applied Psychology: Health and Well-Being*.[9] This is because when we try to go to sleep, worries and anxieties that prey on our minds can stop us enjoying a restful slumber. If, instead, we go to sleep thinking happy thoughts about all the good things in our life, we will be more relaxed and therefore more likely to get to sleep quicker and stay asleep.[10]

6 Gratitude improves self-esteem – a 2014 study of self-esteem (an important contributor to good performance) published in the *Journal of Applied Sport Psychology* found that gratitude increased athletes' self-esteem. Other studies have shown that gratitude reduces social comparisons[11], which can erode self-esteem so much. Instead of comparing ourselves unfavourably to others, being grateful for what we have makes us feel more at peace with and confident in ourselves.

7 Gratitude can even help us overcome trauma – a 2003 study published in the *Journal of Personality and Social Psychology* found that gratitude was a major contributor to resilience following the terrorist attacks on 11 September 2001, while a 2006 study published in *Behavior Research and Therapy* found that Vietnam War veterans with higher levels of gratitude experienced lower rates of post-traumatic stress disorder.[12]

All of these benefits lead to an increase in happiness, so the link between gratitude and happiness is indisputable.

The Skill of Being Grateful

It takes time to learn gratitude and hence it takes time to reap the rewards. Most studies on gratitude show that benefits accrue gradually; you won't suddenly be happy after completing this section of your journal for a day, or even a week. For some people, gratitude does not come easily and thinking of things to write in the journal will be hard and rather forced at first. As your skill develops, it will not only become easier, but you will start to notice things that you are grateful for during the day. This is how developing the skill changes your mindset so that you start thinking differently. Instead of being disappointed with life or feeling let down or even angry with your lot, you will start looking for and noticing the good stuff – the stuff you can be grateful for. Completing this Domain of your journal will become easier as you learn this skill.

Gratitude and Mindfulness

Being grateful for positive, enjoyable things does not mean that we negate the bad stuff that is happening to us. It just changes our focus from being hyper-aware of all the things that we are NOT grateful for to all the things that we are – or can be. This encourages us to live in the moment, a concept adopted by the mindfulness trend.

When we live in the moment, we can value what we have right now, without worrying or being distressed by what has happened before or what might happen in the future. Perhaps you are enjoying a walk in the spring sunshine; you might be worried about your child or you may be plagued with financial worries. But it's sunny now – you can just enjoy the moment and put aside all your cares. Be grateful for that moment in the warm sun, be grateful that you can walk, that you have the freedom to enjoy the sunshine.

Yes, life isn't perfect; yes, you have problems. But there is goodness out there, too, and if we stop to appreciate it, we can enjoy a respite from our anxieties.

APPRECIATE THE MUNDANE

The key to gratitude in this Domain is about valuing and appreciating the mundane. Remember in the Introduction we talked about the Dull Men's Club – people who found pleasure in the ordinary. It is the same principle in this Domain – appreciating and being grateful for the small joys in life, the things that make life run more smoothly, the things that we normally take for granted. This Domain is different from the 'Pleasure' Domain and also from the 'Achievements' or 'Positive Strokes' Domains – while we can be grateful for a lovely cup of coffee or for being able to do a job well or even grateful that we have been appreciated, this Domain is slightly different. It really is more about appreciating those little things that we normally only really notice when they go wrong.

Now go back to the section at the beginning of this Domain where you wrote down what you felt grateful for at that moment. Was there anything 'mundane' in that list? If so, great! If not, add some here:

What 'Mundane' Things Do I Feel Grateful for Right Now?

....

....

....

....

....

....

....

....

When did you last feel grateful that your computer has given you access to the Internet? Or that your phone allows you to send instant text messages? Or that your car got you from A to B? Chances are that unless you have just experienced a breakdown in these systems, you won't give them a second thought. We take for granted that we have the world at our fingertips these days, that we can communicate instantly with almost anyone, that we can hop into a vehicle and be transported somewhere very quickly. Yet when the computer crashes or the phone dies on us or our car breaks down, suddenly we realise how lost we are without these things.

Types of Gratitude

Commentators sometimes talk about different types of gratitude and I think the following distinction can be useful:

Casual Gratitude – this is usually outwardly expressed gratitude for the little things in life. Casual Gratitude is saying thank you to people and showing your appreciation to others

→

for favours, for hard work or even for just doing their job. It is about expressing gratitude to waiters, to shop assistants and to the bus driver, as well as to friends for small favours rendered. Casual Gratitude is about having a grateful and thankful attitude towards life and others, which is very positive. But this is not the sort of gratitude that should be recorded in this journal; expressing thanks to your waiter might go into the Random Acts of Kindness Domain (see Domain 6), but not recorded as 'I am grateful that my waiter served me'.

Deep Gratitude – Deep Gratitude, on the other hand, is exactly what should be recorded here. This is the stuff that, when thought about deeply, we realise we are grateful for (the things we have been discussing in this Domain). We don't usually express Deep Gratitude outwardly, though we may; for example, if a friend does a really huge favour for you, you might write that as a 'thing to be grateful for' ('I am so grateful to have such a good friend' or 'I am grateful that my friend helped me in this way') and, of course, you would also express profuse gratitude to them!

Radical Gratitude – this is a rather different concept that has its roots in religious teachings. Radical Gratitude is about being grateful even when bad things happen. Being grateful for the bad stuff, the knocks, the put-downs and the disappointments is an amazingly resilient attitude to cultivate, but very hard to do. Radical Gratitude is about recognising that we learn from the bad stuff, that we grow from strife and that we need rain to make a rainbow. It is a philosophy that says, 'I am grateful that this bad thing happened because I can grow and learn from it.'

An example of how to practise Radical Gratitude is illustrated by an experience I had while writing this section of the journal. I had to take a break from writing to see some clients at my clinic. One had cancelled but I mistakenly crossed the wrong client off my electronic calendar, which meant that I was happily writing away when they called me on my mobile asking where I was. I realised my mistake, rushed down to my clinic and ended up being half an hour late. Of course, I apologised profusely and did not charge the client for the eventual session, but I felt pretty annoyed with myself for making such a stupid mistake – and frustrated that it cost me a decent amount of money.

But here is how I practised Radical Gratitude; this is what went in this Domain in my Ten-Minute Journal:

> I am grateful that I made this mistake now because I have learned from it – I will always double- and triple-check appointment times so I am sure it won't happen again. This was a reasonably good client for this to happen with because they are established, very kind and forgiving, and were happy in that they got a free session. I am sure they still think highly of me and would still recommend me to others. If this had happened with a new client, or with someone less forgiving, I might have lost a client and perhaps even damaged my professional reputation.

→

This then is Radical Gratitude. It is seeing the good in a bad situation and refusing to let it bring you down. Instead of Radical Gratitude, I could have beaten myself up for being so stupid and for losing money. This would have lowered my self-esteem and mood. Radical Gratitude turns a negative into a positive.

So, practise Radical Gratitude where you can and write these incidents in this Domain. Soon, seeing the good in the bad will become second nature, which will contribute to a general feeling of satisfaction, contentment and, yes, happiness with life – even when things don't go well.

This Domain then is about recognising those things that we normally only notice by their absence. It's only when we are suffering from toothache that we appreciate the joy of being able to eat without pain. We appreciate the sun more after it has rained, our health more after we have been bedridden. Yet these things are the most beautiful gifts – and this Domain is about stopping to appreciate them and value them.

How Gratitude Rewires the Brain

In 2016, researchers recruited 43 participants who were suffering from anxiety or depression. They all attended for counselling but were split into two groups; half spent some of the counselling sessions composing notes of gratitude, which they could choose to send to recipients or just put away somewhere. After three months of this, they were given brain scans, during which they were repeatedly given money that they could choose to donate to charity as a token of their gratitude.

Those who chose to donate money showed profound activity in the frontal, parietal and occipital regions of their brain. But this wasn't the most startling finding. What was really interesting was that the participants who had undertaken the gratitude exercises showed the most brain activity – and this activity was long-lasting, still showing up months later; subjects who participated in gratitude letter-writing showed both behavioural increases in gratitude and significantly greater neural activity during gratitude exercises in the medial prefrontal cortex three months later.[13]

Earlier studies have also shown the effects in brain activity of gratitude. One study in 2008 found that making judgements that incited gratitude elicited activity in the right anterior superior temporal cortex, while a 2014 study found that individual differences in proneness to gratitude correlated with increased grey matter volume in certain areas of the brain. Another study published in the same year found a correlation between individual differences in a genotype for oxytocin (the bonding or 'love' hormone) function and behavioural expressions of gratitude, suggesting that gratitude is important in social bonding and relationship building.[14]

BLESSINGS TO BE COUNTED

Blessings, too, can be classified into rough themes; but again, they might fit more than one theme – the themes that follow over the page are presented as a guide rather than a set structure for you to work with when you complete your journal.

Theme	Example
Technology/car	My iPad crash didn't result in loss of data and it rebooted fine!
	My car passed its MOT.
	My lost work was backed up on the cloud.
	WhatsApp is such a blessing — to be able to contact my family and friends abroad whenever I want at no cost!
	My car started in very icy conditions.
	The virus draining my phone battery was sorted without me having to invest in a new phone.
	The presentation I was giving and couldn't find on my memory stick was retrievable by email.
Health	A good night's sleep at last.
	The pain in my knee has gone.
	I don't have toothache.
	After visiting someone who is sick, I am so grateful that I am healthy.
	My backache has improved.
	My nasty cold has cleared up and not developed into anything worse.
	My blood pressure and cholesterol were OK after a check-up at the doctor.

My dental check-up was OK – no fillings!

The dodgy curry I thought I'd had didn't make me ill.

The annoying sinus problems I have had for ages seem finally to have cleared up.

Disaster averted

Grateful that I found my destination today after getting horribly lost (despite satnav!).

My partner arrived back safely from his trip overseas.

Parked car in rather dodgy place in town so very grateful that it was all in one piece when I went back to it.

Radical gratitude

Although I got a punctured tyre it didn't happen on a day that would have caused me far more stress.

The things that really matter (general things)

I have such good friends.

I have the energy to do so much.

My life is so varied – I never know what each day will bring.

I have such lovely places to explore on my doorstep.

I have enjoyed a rare and special day with my parents.

I have been able to enjoy two lovely weeks in the sun on holiday.

I have received such a thoughtful birthday gift from my grown-up daughter.

I have been able to enjoy such a lovely evening with friends.

I have had a relatively relaxing week.

I am grateful that although there have been threats of redundancy at work, my job is safe.

My business is going well.

We have heating again after the boiler was finally fixed.

I have enjoyed a wonderful Christmas with family and friends.

Specific events
My boss is allowing me to attend a training course I wanted to go on — and is even paying for it.

My son did well in his exams and so will get into the university of his choice.

I managed to get back to sleep after waking up in the early hours.

A gift I ordered arrived in time.

RANDOM ACTS OF KINDNESS

. . . .

This final Domain is surprisingly important. Research has consistently shown that being kind to others and performing good deeds makes us feel good – and can even make us healthier. People who regularly perform good deeds feel that they are contributing to society and that they have a purpose in their life. Making other people's lives that bit better will also make our own life better, too – so we should try to perform and record at least one Random Act of Kindness each day. We will also build a lovely record of all the good we have done, which should banish any of those 'I am useless' thoughts that so many people have.

Take a moment now to think about and note down all the Random Acts of Kindness you have thoughtfully done for others over the last couple of weeks:

Random Acts of Kindness I've Done for Others Recently

....

....

....

....

....

....

....

....

IF I DO SOMETHING NICE, I MUST BE NICE

Doing something nice for other people strengthens our perceptions of ourselves as someone nice and caring – 'If I do something nice for another person, I must be a nice, kind, caring person ...' – and it makes us feel good. Not just good – but actually happy. A Japanese study in 2006 showed that kind people experience more happiness and have happier memories than less kind people.[1] The research showed that simply noting and counting acts of kindness for a week, like we are doing in this Ten-Minute Programme, can make us happier. This could be because being kind makes us value ourselves as good people and therefore makes us feel subjectively positive; by counting our acts of kindness in a week, we are reminding ourselves how nice we are and so we are able to enhance our own self-esteem. Even the thought of helping others makes us happier and there are physiological reasons for this; brain scans show that thinking about helping activates the mesolimbic pathway in the brain – a pathway associated with happiness via the production of the neurotransmitter called dopamine.[2]

I am doing something kind ➡ therefore I must be kind – a good person ➡ It feels good to be a good person. I feel happy

So powerful is the effect of performing good deeds on happiness levels that research in the UK has even gone so far as to show that being kind can reduce depression.[3] This led one public health body[4] to wonder whether volunteering or performing good deeds should be an advised public health intervention; in other words, instead of handing out antidepressant medication, perhaps doctors should be prescribing an hour of volunteering a week to help their depressed patients. Which is exactly the point of the Ten-Minute Programme!

Get That Helper's High

This good, happy feeling associated with acts of kindness is so well established that it has even got its own name – the 'helper's high' or the 'giver's glow'. This term was popularised in a 1988 *Psychology Today* article (although it may have originated as long ago as 1979) in which a total of 3,299 volunteers were analysed and found to exhibit a strong physical response from their good work that was thought to be similar to that experienced after exercise or meditation.[5] Another study identified high levels of the 'bonding' hormone oxytocin in people who are very generous towards others. Oxytocin is the hormone best known for its ability to help new mothers bond with their babies and has also been shown to cause the release of a chemical called nitric oxide in blood vessels, which expands the blood vessels; this reduces blood pressure.[6] Oxytocin may even slow down the ageing process because it reduces levels of free radicals and inflammation in the cardiovascular system and thus 'slows ageing at its source'.[7] So, performing acts of kindness should not only make you feel happy, it might make you feel and look younger, too!

Boost Self-Esteem

Many people who suffer from low mood or depression also experience low self-esteem. Low self-esteem is pretty endemic in today's 'Facebook Society', where everything we do is measured by how many 'likes' we have. Ratcheting up the likes can be an absorbing business – and one that can be damaging to fragile self-esteem. Never before have we been in a climate where social comparison is not only so easy, but all-pervasive (and even measurable). It used to be, a few generations ago, that the only people we could compare ourselves to were our neighbours – people who lived like us and worked like us. Perhaps one neighbour would get a better oven or furniture, or another would go on a trip to the seaside but, in the main, we felt satisfied that we were no worse off than most of the people we knew.

Nowadays, with social mobility and social media, we can compare ourselves to a much wider pool of people; in fact, to an infinite pool. Not only can we compare ourselves to friends and acquaintances across the globe, but to celebrities, too. And these people post the edited highlights of their lives on Facebook so all we see are the holidays, parties, fabulous clothes and exotic meals out that they are experiencing. Is it any wonder that our own lives can seem so dull in comparison? Is it any wonder that so many of us feel worthless and undervalued when the exciting lives that everyone else seems to be living are thrust in front of our eyes on a daily basis? This was discussed more in the Introduction, but the result of this low self-esteem is that people feel worthless, useless and 'good for nothing'.

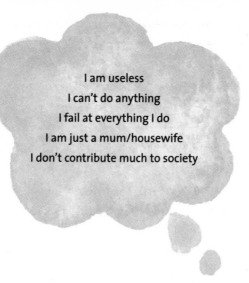

I am useless
I can't do anything
I fail at everything I do
I am just a mum/housewife
I don't contribute much to society

COMMON THINGS PEOPLE WITH LOW SELF-ESTEEM SAY OR THINK

All this can be changed by the simple act of performing a good deed. Suddenly, you have to acknowledge that you did something good, that you made a difference to someone's life. The more good deeds you do, the bigger the difference you make – and the better you feel.

I am useless ➡ But if I help someone I can't be that useless ➡ I made a difference to someones life – I am of value ➡ I feel better about myself

As an experiment, see if you can do something nice or kind for someone and make a note here about what you did and how it made you feel:

What Act of Kindness Did I Do, and
How Did It Make Me Feel?

....

....

....

....

....

....

....

....

....

But I Am in Physical Pain – How Can Good Deeds Help with That?

Many clients whom I have seen over the years are depressed because they are suffering from physical ill health. There is nothing like being in constant pain to make you feel down. Yet performing acts of kindness can even help with that. In a 2002 study published in *Pain Management Nursing*[8], researchers found that patients with chronic pain experienced less pain, depression and disability when they counselled and helped other patients.

Helping others could be so beneficial to our health that it might even save our lives. In another study, this time at the Buck Institute for Age Research in California, elderly volunteers who helped out for more than 4 hours per week were 44 per cent less likely to die during the course of the study than those who didn't.[9] And a study that followed 427 married women over a period of 30 years found that 52 per cent of those who did not volunteer experienced a major illness, compared with only 36 per cent who did volunteer.[10]

Being kind may exert its health benefits by lowering the number of stress hormones we produce; a study in Miami of patients with HIV showed that altruistic patients had lower levels of stress hormones.[11] In another study, older adults who volunteered to give a massage to babies also had lowered stress hormones.[12] Being kind may also stimulate the production of protective antibodies and, in fact, even witnessing someone else being kind might be enough to produce this effect; when researchers at Harvard University showed people a film about Mother Teresa's work, they discovered an increase in the production of protective antibodies, when compared with another group who watched a neutral film.[13]

Good Deeds Help Us Focus Outwards Instead of Inwards

When we feel down, it is easy to become very focused on our own misery. By forcing ourselves to perform a good deed for someone, who, by definition, needs it, we are ensuring that we start looking around us for needy recipients, to start feeling their need and to loosen the obsession with our own unhappiness. And, of course, helping others less fortunate than ourselves helps put our own problems in perspective.

Depressed people are often in the habit of being on the receiving end of help, advice and input, which can make them feel indebted and uncomfortable. Giving back redresses the balance and thus enhances self-esteem. Performing kind acts means that the depressed person needs to get back into society – it is hard to be kind if you don't interact with people. Depressed people are often socially isolated or withdrawn, so this is a way to increase their involvement with others.

IDEAS FOR PERFORMING ACTS OF KINDNESS

The acts of kindness you can perform for this Ten-Minute Programme do not have to be earth-shattering or even terribly expansive. It is true that one of the most important parts of therapy programmes that I develop with depressed clients involves encouraging some form of volunteering, but it also has to be acknowledged that many clients are not ready (or lack the time) to leap straight into a regular, time-consuming commitment. Volunteering to help in your local charity shop a morning a week, visiting a local care home for an hour a week, helping schoolchildren with their reading an afternoon a week – these are fabulous activities that will undoubtedly make the giver feel better and prove they are valued and valuable members of society. But this is often too big a step to start with for many. People suffering from low self-esteem often feel they have little to offer, or lack confidence to make such a commitment. So, it is always better to start small, with tiny acts of kindness that can be acknowledged and noted in the journal. As you get used to this, you will start looking for kind things to do in order to have things to write – this is how the Ten-Minute Programme can change your life!

And, even better, as you progress, you will have a permanent record of all the acts of kindness you have performed during the course of the programme. If those self-doubts ever creep back in, dig out this journal and look back at the positive difference you have made to so many people's lives. This will be the proof of your worth – and that should lift your spirits.

Some Ideas to Get You Started

(taken from my e-book *Paying It Forward*)

* Pay for someone's cup of coffee
* Get the next person's food, toll, petrol, etc.
* Buy food for a homeless person
* Offer your professional services (e.g. hairdressing, free family portrait, etc.)
* Volunteer at school
* Hold the door open for someone
* Pay someone's bus fare
* Smile at people
* Share your umbrella with a stranger
* Give someone your parking space
* Ask for charitable donations instead of birthday gifts
* Stop if you see someone broken down and give them some biscuits or food
* Put change in an expiring car park meter
* Offer to take photos of people who are taking photos of each other
* Take flowers to a hospital and give to someone who hasn't got any
* Write letters to the media praising organisations
* Give money to a busker
* Sit and chat to a homeless person
* Recommend a local business
* Share your friends – introduce them to other people
* Put neighbours' bins out/wash their car/mow their lawn
* Hand balloons out to kids
    →

* Blow bubbles in the street
* Help someone carry/pack their groceries
* Tape the money for a chocolate bar on a vending machine
* Reverse trick or treat
* Buy twelve flowers; keep one and pass the rest on
* Bake cookies and give to neighbours
* Write 'thank you' cards for teachers – not just at the end of the year
* Say something nice to someone every day
* Talk to someone who is lonely

ACTS OF KINDNESS

There are so many things that you can record here – little or big.
You might have a regular volunteering commitment (if not, maybe
consider getting one!) so if that's the case, don't put that down
every single time. Just write that when there is nothing else to
write. But aim to have something to write down every single day.

*I spent an hour chatting to a lonely old lady in her
home today.*

I went into my kids' school to listen to children read.

I volunteer at our local old people's home.

*I made a point this week of contacting everyone I know on
Facebook who has been having troubles – seeing how they
are and what the latest situation is.*

I donated money to someone doing a fun run for charity.

*I set up a JustGiving account to donate to charity
more easily.*

I wrote a nice review of a restaurant on TripAdvisor.

I went to visit someone who has recently been bereaved.

*I bought something from a friend trying to set up a new
business – I wanted to encourage her.*

*I visited a neighbour who had suffered a bad fall, and took
a home-made meal.*

→

A friend asked me to lend him some money and I didn't hesitate.

I did some shopping for an elderly neighbour.

I did some work for free for a family who couldn't afford to pay.

I gave a lift to an acquaintance even though it took me well out of my way and added an extra 20 minutes to my journey.

I donated two bags of old clothes to a charity shop (instead of selling them).

I sent someone who has had problems a card just to let her know I am thinking of her.

I gave blood today.

I went into our local nature reserve and picked up litter.

I took part in a bake sale for charity.

I bought an extra sandwich today and gave it to a homeless man in town.

I let someone with only a few items go in front of me in the supermarket.

I gave someone the benefit of the doubt today.

I went into my child's school to talk about my job as part of a project on career options.

I had some wedding photos and I printed out extra copies of some of the guests and sent them to them.

I donated a pile of books to our local bookshare club.

Colleagues were saying really spiteful things about another person we work with. I chimed in by saying something nice about them.

I made sure to say hello and stop to talk to the cleaners and security guards at work.

I gave someone who is looking for work some odd jobs to do.

I introduced a friend to a work colleague who I thought would be useful to them.

I wrote a nice review on Amazon of a book I enjoyed.

I had a spare discount voucher for a theme park so I gave it to someone in the queue.

I don't want the free collectable cards you get at the supermarket but I know a friends child who does so I collected a pile and took them round.

I saw a couple trying to take a selfie — I asked if they would like me to take the photo and they happily accepted my offer.

THE JOURNAL

....

DATE OR WEEK COMMENCING

....

DOMAIN 1 PLEASURE
Things that I enjoyed

....

....

....

....

....

....

....

DOMAIN 2 POSITIVE STROKES
Praise that I received

....

....

....

....

....

....

....

DOMAIN 3 LUCKY ME
Good fortune that I experienced

....

....

....

....

....

....

DOMAIN 4 ACHIEVEMENTS
Things that made me think 'well done me!'

....
....
....
....
....
....
....

DOMAIN 5 GRATITUDE
Blessings that I am grateful for

....
....
....
....
....
....
....

DOMAIN 6 RANDOM ACTS OF KINDNESS
Moments of kindness that I have performed

....
....
....
....
....
....
....

NOTES

....
....

DATE OR WEEK COMMENCING

....

DOMAIN 1 PLEASURE
Things that I enjoyed

....

....

....

....

....

....

....

DOMAIN 2 POSITIVE STROKES
Praise that I received

....

....

....

....

....

....

....

DOMAIN 3 LUCKY ME
Good fortune that I experienced

....

....

....

....

....

....

....

DOMAIN 4 ACHIEVEMENTS
Things that made me think 'well done me!'

....

....

....

....

....

....

....

DOMAIN 5 GRATITUDE
Blessings that I am grateful for

....

....

....

....

....

....

....

DOMAIN 6 RANDOM ACTS OF KINDNESS
Moments of kindness that I have performed

....

....

....

....

....

....

....

NOTES

....

....

We Need to Be Sad Sometimes Too: Here's Why[1]

*   Sadness can improve memory – in a study, people in a bad mood due to rainy, cold weather remembered more items in a shop than happier people did on a lovely sunny day. It seems that being in a negative, downcast mood actually leads us to pay more attention and therefore be better able to recall things.

*   Sadness can improve our social judgements – we are always judging others in order to predict and make sense of our social world. But these judgements can be wrong due to shortcuts and biases that humans are prone to making. And research has shown that we are more likely to make those mistakes when we are happy.

*   Sadness can motivate us – we are motivated to find happiness and therefore change things that are making us sad (this is why you have bought this Ten-Minute Programme). Researchers conducted a study that showed sad people were more likely to persevere at difficult questions than happy people; this may be because happy people are less motivated to succeed at something when they are already happy.

....

Who Is Happy?

According to psychology professor Sonja Lyubomirsky, author of *The How of Happiness*, about 50 per cent of our happiness quotient is down to our baseline happiness level, which is something we're born with. In other words, some people are just naturally happier than others. Another 10 per cent can be accounted for by life circumstances, which include our financial situation. The rest of our happiness is caused by 'intentional daily activities – those things we do to make us happier'.[2]

The Ten-Minute Programme to happiness can boost that 40 per cent.

....

DATE OR WEEK COMMENCING

....

DOMAIN 1 PLEASURE
Things that I enjoyed

....
....
....
....
....
....
....

DOMAIN 2 POSITIVE STROKES
Praise that I received

....
....
....
....
....
....
....

DOMAIN 3 LUCKY ME
Good fortune that I experienced

....
....
....
....
....
....
....

DOMAIN 4 ACHIEVEMENTS
Things that made me think 'well done me!'

....

....

....

....

....

....

....

DOMAIN 5 GRATITUDE
Blessings that I am grateful for

....

....

....

....

....

....

....

DOMAIN 6 RANDOM ACTS OF KINDNESS
Moments of kindness that I have performed

....

....

....

....

....

....

....

NOTES

....

....

DATE OR WEEK COMMENCING

....

DOMAIN 1 PLEASURE
Things that I enjoyed

....
....
....
....
....
....
....

DOMAIN 2 POSITIVE STROKES
Praise that I received

....
....
....
....
....
....
....

DOMAIN 3 LUCKY ME
Good fortune that I experienced

....
....
....
....
....
....

DOMAIN 4 ACHIEVEMENTS
Things that made me think 'well done me!'

....

....

....

....

....

....

....

DOMAIN 5 GRATITUDE
Blessings that I am grateful for

....

....

....

....

....

....

....

DOMAIN 6 RANDOM ACTS OF KINDNESS
Moments of kindness that I have performed

....

....

....

....

....

....

....

NOTES

....

....

We Need Meaningful Experiences to Be Happy

In his best-selling book, *Man's Search for Meaning*, Viktor Frankl described his time spent in a Nazi concentration camp and how he managed to survive despite losing all of the family members he was imprisoned with. The secret was finding meaning in even the most horrific circumstances, which he said made him more resilient to suffering.

....

Where Does Happiness Live in the Brain?

The area of the brain responsible for feelings of
happiness is the hippocampus. Serotonin and
dopamine are two neurotransmitters in the
brain that are thought to be important in the
regulation of our feelings of happiness.

....

....

DOMAIN 1 PLEASURE
Things that I enjoyed

....

....

....

....

....

....

....

DOMAIN 2 POSITIVE STROKES
Praise that I received

....

....

....

....

....

....

....

DOMAIN 3 LUCKY ME
Good fortune that I experienced

....

....

....

....

....

....

....

DOMAIN 4 ACHIEVEMENTS
Things that made me think 'well done me!'

....
....
....
....
....
....
....

DOMAIN 5 GRATITUDE
Blessings that I am grateful for

....
....
....
....
....
....
....

DOMAIN 6 RANDOM ACTS OF KINDNESS
Moments of kindness that I have performed

....
....
....
....
....
....
....

NOTES

....
....

....

DOMAIN 1 PLEASURE
Things that I enjoyed

....
....
....
....
....
....
....

DOMAIN 2 POSITIVE STROKES
Praise that I received

....
....
....
....
....
....
....

DOMAIN 3 LUCKY ME
Good fortune that I experienced

....
....
....
....
....
....

DOMAIN 4 ACHIEVEMENTS
Things that made me think 'well done me!'

....
....
....
....
....
....
....

DOMAIN 5 GRATITUDE
Blessings that I am grateful for

....
....
....
....
....
....
....

DOMAIN 6 RANDOM ACTS OF KINDNESS
Moments of kindness that I have performed

....
....
....
....
....
....
....

NOTES

....
....

DATE OR WEEK COMMENCING

....

DOMAIN 1 PLEASURE
Things that I enjoyed

....

....

....

....

....

....

DOMAIN 2 POSITIVE STROKES
Praise that I received

....

....

....

....

....

....

DOMAIN 3 LUCKY ME
Good fortune that I experienced

....

....

....

....

....

....

Domain 4 ACHIEVEMENTS
Things that made me think 'well done me!'

....

....

....

....

....

....

....

Domain 5 GRATITUDE
Blessings that I am grateful for

....

....

....

....

....

....

....

Domain 6 RANDOM ACTS OF KINDNESS
Moments of kindness that I have performed

....

....

....

....

....

....

....

NOTES

....

....

In his 2007 book *Stumbling on to Happiness*, Dan Gilbert says there are three key findings on the science of happiness:

1 We can't be happy alone

2 We can't be happy all the time

3 We can be happier than we are currently

Does Money Buy Us Happiness?

Yes – but only up to a point. Psychologist Daniel Kahneman and economist Angus Deaton, both from Princeton University, showed that self-reported levels of well-being increased with salaries of up to $75,000 (roughly £50,000) a year. But after that, increasing amounts of money had no further effect on happiness.[3]

DATE OR WEEK COMMENCING

....

DOMAIN 1 PLEASURE
Things that I enjoyed

....

....

....

....

....

....

....

DOMAIN 2 POSITIVE STROKES
Praise that I received

....

....

....

....

....

....

....

DOMAIN 3 LUCKY ME
Good fortune that I experienced

....

....

....

....

....

....

....

Domain 4 Achievements
Things that made me think 'well done me!'

....
....
....
....
....
....
....

Domain 5 Gratitude
Blessings that I am grateful for

....
....
....
....
....
....
....

Domain 6 Random Acts of Kindness
Moments of kindness that I have performed

....
....
....
....
....
....
....

Notes

....
....

DATE OR WEEK COMMENCING

....

DOMAIN 1 PLEASURE
Things that I enjoyed

....
....
....
....
....
....
....
....

DOMAIN 2 POSITIVE STROKES
Praise that I received

....
....
....
....
....
....
....
....

DOMAIN 3 LUCKY ME
Good fortune that I experienced

....
....
....
....
....
....
....

DOMAIN 4 ACHIEVEMENTS
Things that made me think 'well done me!'

....
....
....
....
....
....
....

DOMAIN 5 GRATITUDE
Blessings that I am grateful for

....
....
....
....
....
....
....

DOMAIN 6 RANDOM ACTS OF KINDNESS
Moments of kindness that I have performed

....
....
....
....
....
....
....

NOTES

....
....

....

A Day to Be Happy

In 2012 at the first ever UN conference on
Happiness, the United Nations declared
20 March the International Day of Happiness
to recognise the relevance of happiness
and well-being as universal goals.
All 193 United Nations member states have
adopted a resolution calling for happiness to
be given greater priority. It is coordinated by
Action for Happiness, a non-profit movement
of people from 160 countries.

....

Why Overindulgence is NOT the Key to Happiness

According to the 'hedonic treadmill' (or 'hedonic adaptation') hypothesis, just as we adjust our walking or running speed to match the speed of the treadmill, we adjust our moods to match whatever life throws at us.

Evidence for this comes from studies investigating people who have experienced either extremely positive (group 1) or extremely negative (group 2) life events. People in group 1 are happier than people in group 2, but often for very short periods. For example, big lottery winners report being extremely happy after winning the lottery. However, their happiness falls to baseline levels about two months later. This is because when a person has more money, expectations and desires rise in tandem, which results in no permanent gain in happiness. Conversely, people unfortunate enough to become paralysed from the waist down return to almost baseline levels of happiness within a few months of the accident.[4]

Hedonic adaptation can also explain why overindulging rarely makes us happy. We get accustomed to new happy experiences fairly quickly and then our happiness level usually goes back to where it was before. I imagine that if I ate chocolate all day, I would feel very happy, but research actually suggests that eating less would make me happier than eating more,[5] possibly because I would appreciate it more and not simply adapt to the pleasure of it.

Similarly, whilst most of us think that being on holiday for ever, or giving up work for ever would be heaven, the reality would probably be very different – after the initial high, we would simply adapt and get used to the new situation and our happiness levels would drop again. Thus, if we crave happiness, we should be moderate in fulfilling our desires.

DATE OR WEEK COMMENCING

....

DOMAIN 1 PLEASURE
Things that I enjoyed

....

....

....

....

....

....

....

....

DOMAIN 2 POSITIVE STROKES
Praise that I received

....

....

....

....

....

....

....

DOMAIN 3 LUCKY ME
Good fortune that I experienced

....

....

....

....

....

....

DOMAIN 4 ACHIEVEMENTS
Things that made me think 'well done me!'

....

....

....

....

....

....

....

DOMAIN 5 GRATITUDE
Blessings that I am grateful for

....

....

....

....

....

....

....

DOMAIN 6 RANDOM ACTS OF KINDNESS
Moments of kindness that I have performed

....

....

....

....

....

....

....

NOTES

....

....

....

DOMAIN 1 PLEASURE
Things that I enjoyed

....
....
....
....
....
....
....
....

DOMAIN 2 POSITIVE STROKES
Praise that I received

....
....
....
....
....
....
....
....

DOMAIN 3 LUCKY ME
Good fortune that I experienced

....
....
....
....
....
....
....

DOMAIN 4 ACHIEVEMENTS
Things that made me think 'well done me!'

....
....
....
....
....
....
....

DOMAIN 5 GRATITUDE
Blessings that I am grateful for

....
....
....
....
....
....
....

DOMAIN 6 RANDOM ACTS OF KINDNESS
Moments of kindness that I have performed

....
....
....
....
....
....
....

NOTES

....
....

What Does 'Happiness' Actually Mean?

We all want to be happy, but being happy can mean different things to different people. One person might be happy being a drug addict or making other people unhappy. My kids would be happy missing school and engaging with their devices all day. As for me, spending several hours eating chocolate would make me very happy.

But these are all short-term feelings of happiness. I suspect that after three hours of solid chocolate-eating I would no longer be happy. My children might be happy on their devices for longer than a few hours but ten years down the line with no qualifications and no prospects, they would be unlikely still to be happy. As for the drug addict, would he even be alive to be happy ten years later?

Clearly, the things we do in the short term to make us happy do not guarantee long-term happiness. Happiness should not be confused with the more fleeting experiences of pleasure. Clearly, chasing pleasure does not always bring happiness.

Aristotle conceived of happiness as being made up of hedonia (pleasure) and eudaimonia (a life well lived). The hedonia is probably akin to the short-term chocolate-eating that I would love to indulge in, whereas the eudaimonia refers to a healthy lifestyle that would probably make me happier in the longer term. Living a meaningful life probably comes under the eudaimonia heading, too.

Positive psychologists such as Dr Martin Seligman have recently added one more distinct component to the definition of happiness: engagement. Engagement refers to living a 'good life' balanced with meaningful work, family, friends and hobbies.

Happiness is usually measured subjectively – by simply asking people to rate how happy they feel, perhaps on a scale of 0–100, where 0 is very unhappy and 100 is the happiest you have ever felt. You could try this throughout the Ten-Minute Programme so you can track the changes to your happiness levels.

....

DOMAIN 1 PLEASURE
Things that I enjoyed

....

....

....

....

....

....

....

....

DOMAIN 2 POSITIVE STROKES
Praise that I received

....

....

....

....

....

....

....

DOMAIN 3 LUCKY ME
Good fortune that I experienced

....

....

....

....

....

....

....

Domain 4 Achievements
Things that made me think 'well done me!'

....

....

....

....

....

....

....

Domain 5 Gratitude
Blessings that I am grateful for

....

....

....

....

....

....

....

Domain 6 Random Acts of Kindness
Moments of kindness that I have performed

....

....

....

....

....

....

....

Notes

....

....

DATE OR WEEK COMMENCING

....

DOMAIN 1 PLEASURE
Things that I enjoyed

....
....
....
....
....
....
....
....

DOMAIN 2 POSITIVE STROKES
Praise that I received

....
....
....
....
....
....
....

DOMAIN 3 LUCKY ME
Good fortune that I experienced

....
....
....
....
....
....

DOMAIN 4 ACHIEVEMENTS
Things that made me think 'well done me!'

....
....
....
....
....
....
....

DOMAIN 5 GRATITUDE
Blessings that I am grateful for

....
....
....
....
....
....
....

DOMAIN 6 RANDOM ACTS OF KINDNESS
Moments of kindness that I have performed

....
....
....
....
....
....
....

NOTES

....
....

....

DOMAIN 1 PLEASURE
Things that I enjoyed

....
....
....
....
....
....
....
....

DOMAIN 2 POSITIVE STROKES
Praise that I received

....
....
....
....
....
....
....
....

DOMAIN 3 LUCKY ME
Good fortune that I experienced

....
....
....
....
....
....
....
....

Domain 4 Achievements
Things that made me think 'well done me!'

....
....
....
....
....
....

Domain 5 Gratitude
Blessings that I am grateful for

....
....
....
....
....
....

Domain 6 Random Acts of Kindness
Moments of kindness that I have performed

....
....
....
....
....
....

Notes

....
....

What Makes Us Happy?

1 Pleasure (tasty food, warm baths, etc.)

2 Engagement (or flow, the absorption of an enjoyed yet challenging activity)

3 Relationships (social ties have turned out to be an extremely reliable indicator of happiness)

4 Meaning (a perceived quest or belonging to something bigger)

5 Accomplishments (having realised tangible goals).[6]

Top Twenty Things That Make Us Happy

In 2016 researchers from the University of Sussex and the London School of Economics asked 20,000 people to download a 'Mappiness' app which sent them a 'ping' at various times of day, and invited them to record their happiness levels and what they were doing at the time.[7] Here are the top 20 things that made people happy (in order):

* Intimacy, making love
* Theatre, dance, concert
* Exhibition, museum, library
* Sports, running, exercise
* Gardening, allotment
* Singing, performing
* Talking, chatting, socialising
* Birdwatching, nature-watching
* Walking, hiking
* Hunting, fishing
* Drinking alcohol
* Hobbies, arts, crafts
* Meditating, religious activities
* Match, sporting event
* Childcare, playing with children
* Pet care, playing with pets
* Listening to music
* Other games, puzzles
* Shopping, errands
* Gambling, betting

....

DOMAIN 1 PLEASURE
Things that I enjoyed

....
....
....
....
....
....
....
....

DOMAIN 2 POSITIVE STROKES
Praise that I received

....
....
....
....
....
....
....

DOMAIN 3 LUCKY ME
Good fortune that I experienced

....
....
....
....
....
....

DOMAIN 4 ACHIEVEMENTS
Things that made me think 'well done me!'

....
....
....
....
....
....
....

DOMAIN 5 GRATITUDE
Blessings that I am grateful for

....
....
....
....
....
....

DOMAIN 6 RANDOM ACTS OF KINDNESS
Moments of kindness that I have performed

....
....
....
....
....
....
....

NOTES

....
....

....

DOMAIN 1 PLEASURE
Things that I enjoyed

....
....
....
....
....
....
....

DOMAIN 2 POSITIVE STROKES
Praise that I received

....
....
....
....
....
....
....

DOMAIN 3 LUCKY ME
Good fortune that I experienced

....
....
....
....
....
....
....

DOMAIN 4 ACHIEVEMENTS
Things that made me think 'well done me!'

....

....

....

....

....

....

....

DOMAIN 5 GRATITUDE
Blessings that I am grateful for

....

....

....

....

....

....

....

DOMAIN 6 RANDOM ACTS OF KINDNESS
Moments of kindness that I have performed

....

....

....

....

....

....

....

NOTES

....

....

Professor Stephen Hawking – Lucky or Unlucky?

Amyotrophic lateral sclerosis (ALS) is a neuromuscular disease that attacks motor neurons causing muscle weakness, atrophy and paralysis. You might expect sufferers to feel terribly unlucky with their lot. Yet Professor Stephen Hawking, one of the best-known sufferers of ALS, believed he was lucky; 'I was lucky to have chosen to work in theoretical physics, because that was one of the few areas in which my condition would not be a serious handicap.'[8]

This reminds me of a dear friend I see every week called Manya. A Holocaust survivor, her entire family, except one brother, was murdered. Among her lost relatives were her parents and two sisters. Yet never a week goes by without her telling me how blessed and lucky she feels. Instead of focusing on her tragic losses, she concentrates on her blessings – her life and her children.

Luck, it seems, is an attitude.

Noting Achievements Builds Self-Esteem

Psychologists recognise two types of self-esteem (SE); global and situational:

Global SE – this is the fairly constant view that we have of our self-worth and tends to be quite stable over time. Global SE is about who we are.

Situational SE – this, on the other hand, is more variable and relates to specific situations. It is thus more about what we are doing than who we are. So, for example, a person might have low SE at home but have a much higher SE at work. Or they may have poor SE when it comes to IT or computer work, but a higher SE when it comes to writing reports. Situational SE is more akin to self-confidence than Global SE is.

....

DOMAIN 1 PLEASURE
Things that I enjoyed

....

....

....

....

....

....

....

DOMAIN 2 POSITIVE STROKES
Praise that I received

....

....

....

....

....

....

....

DOMAIN 3 LUCKY ME
Good fortune that I experienced

....

....

....

....

....

....

DOMAIN 4 ACHIEVEMENTS
Things that made me think 'well done me!'

....

....

....

....

....

....

....

DOMAIN 5 GRATITUDE
Blessings that I am grateful for

....

....

....

....

....

....

....

DOMAIN 6 RANDOM ACTS OF KINDNESS
Moments of kindness that I have performed

....

....

....

....

....

....

....

NOTES

....

....

....

DOMAIN 1 PLEASURE
Things that I enjoyed

....
....
....
....
....
....
....

DOMAIN 2 POSITIVE STROKES
Praise that I received

....
....
....
....
....
....
....

DOMAIN 3 LUCKY ME
Good fortune that I experienced

....
....
....
....
....
....
....

DOMAIN 4 ACHIEVEMENTS
Things that made me think 'well done me!'

....

....

....

....

....

....

....

DOMAIN 5 GRATITUDE
Blessings that I am grateful for

....

....

....

....

....

....

....

DOMAIN 6 RANDOM ACTS OF KINDNESS
Moments of kindness that I have performed

....

....

....

....

....

....

....

NOTES

....

....

Tips to Get Lucky

* Network – talk to people and stay in touch with them
* Join LinkedIn, Facebook and social media with a view to making positive contributions
* Be friendly to strangers; you never know what might happen!
* Smile more and make eye contact more as this can lead to more social encounters (which can lead to more opportunities)
* Develop a natural curiosity
* Look for opportunities everywhere
* Notice things; take your eyes off your phone and look around you more
* Practise seeing things from different viewpoints by playing devil's advocate with some of your own beliefs
* Get out of the rut; change your habits and do things differently sometimes
* Learn to relax a bit more

....

Why Being Kind Makes Us Happy

Performing acts of kindness has consistently been shown to be related to being more satisfied with life.[9] One study, for example, showed that when people performed five kind acts each week for six weeks they experienced an increase in happiness[10] when compared with people who did not perform these acts of kindness. This could be because, as suggested earlier, being nice makes us feel better about ourselves.

....

....

DOMAIN 1 PLEASURE
Things that I enjoyed

....

....

....

....

....

....

....

....

DOMAIN 2 POSITIVE STROKES
Praise that I received

....

....

....

....

....

....

....

....

DOMAIN 3 LUCKY ME
Good fortune that I experienced

....

....

....

....

....

....

....

....

DOMAIN 4 ACHIEVEMENTS
Things that made me think 'well done me!'

....
....
....
....
....
....
....

DOMAIN 5 GRATITUDE
Blessings that I am grateful for

....
....
....
....
....
....
....

DOMAIN 6 RANDOM ACTS OF KINDNESS
Moments of kindness that I have performed

....
....
....
....
....
....
....

NOTES

....
....

....

DOMAIN 1 PLEASURE
Things that I enjoyed

....
....
....
....
....
....
....

DOMAIN 2 POSITIVE STROKES
Praise that I received

....
....
....
....
....
....
....

DOMAIN 3 LUCKY ME
Good fortune that I experienced

....
....
....
....
....
....
....

Domain 4 Achievements
Things that made me think 'well done me!'

....
....
....
....
....
....
....

Domain 5 Gratitude
Blessings that I am grateful for

....
....
....
....
....
....

Domain 6 Random Acts of Kindness
Moments of kindness that I have performed

....
....
....
....
....
....

Notes

....
....

DATE OR WEEK COMMENCING

....

DOMAIN 1 PLEASURE
Things that I enjoyed

....
....
....
....
....
....
....
....

DOMAIN 2 POSITIVE STROKES
Praise that I received

....
....
....
....
....
....
....

DOMAIN 3 LUCKY ME
Good fortune that I experienced

....
....
....
....
....
....
....

DOMAIN 4 ACHIEVEMENTS
Things that made me think 'well done me!'

....

....

....

....

....

....

....

DOMAIN 5 GRATITUDE
Blessings that I am grateful for

....

....

....

....

....

....

....

DOMAIN 6 RANDOM ACTS OF KINDNESS
Moments of kindness that I have performed

....

....

....

....

....

....

....

NOTES

....

....

....

Even Being Kind at Work Can Make Us Happy

Performing acts of kindness can make us happy – not just with life, but even at work, too. According to a study from the University of Wisconsin-Madison in 2013, individuals who rated helping others in their work as important reported they were happier with their life when surveyed thirty years later. This led the researchers to conclude that 'helping others makes us happier'.[11]

....

Why Acts of Kindness Make Us Happy

A study at the University of British Columbia, in Vancouver, Canada, was carried out on 9–11-year-olds to see what would happen when they performed acts of kindness for four weeks. As expected, those who performed the kind deeds ended up feeling happier than those who didn't.

But what was really interesting was that these kids were also more accepting and tolerant of their peers than those who hadn't performed the random acts of kindness.[12] Being kind, then, seems to make us nicer people; perhaps this works via a self-fulfilling prophecy mechanism whereby we notice that we have done something nice and thus conclude that we must be a good person – and good people are accepting and tolerant of others.

....

DOMAIN 1 PLEASURE
Things that I enjoyed

....

....

....

....

....

....

....

DOMAIN 2 POSITIVE STROKES
Praise that I received

....

....

....

....

....

....

....

DOMAIN 3 LUCKY ME
Good fortune that I experienced

....

....

....

....

....

....

DOMAIN 4 ACHIEVEMENTS
Things that made me think 'well done me!'

....
....
....
....
....
....
....

DOMAIN 5 GRATITUDE
Blessings that I am grateful for

....
....
....
....
....
....

DOMAIN 6 RANDOM ACTS OF KINDNESS
Moments of kindness that I have performed

....
....
....
....
....
....
....

NOTES

....
....

DATE OR WEEK COMMENCING

....

DOMAIN 1 PLEASURE
Things that I enjoyed

....

....

....

....

....

....

....

DOMAIN 2 POSITIVE STROKES
Praise that I received

....

....

....

....

....

....

....

DOMAIN 3 LUCKY ME
Good fortune that I experienced

....

....

....

....

....

....

....

DOMAIN 4 ACHIEVEMENTS
Things that made me think 'well done me!'

....
....
....
....
....
....
....

DOMAIN 5 GRATITUDE
Blessings that I am grateful for

....
....
....
....
....
....
....

DOMAIN 6 RANDOM ACTS OF KINDNESS
Moments of kindness that I have performed

....
....
....
....
....
....
....

NOTES

....
....

Performing Good Deeds Becomes a Habit

A study published in the fabulously named *Journal of Happiness Studies* in 2011 showed that when people performed small acts of kindness every day for 5–15 minutes for a week their happiness and self-esteem increased.[13] Of the original 700 recruits, 458 people aged 18–73 completed the first week's exercise, which required them to help or interact with another person every day – someone they knew or a stranger – 'in a supportive and considerate' way.

The positive effects on their happiness and self-esteem were significant. After six months, when the study ended, there were 179 responses with most still doing a good deed one to three days a week and feeling happier for it. Performing good deeds becomes a habit – it might start off as a chore or deliberate exercise, but it becomes second nature after a while. And that means that happiness does, too.

....

Being Kind Can Even Reduce Pain

Cami Walker, a multiple sclerosis sufferer
from Los Angeles, decided to perform an act
of kindness every day for a month – and was
startled by the results (documented in her book
*29 Gifts: How a Month of Giving Can Change
Your Life*). She found that being kind helped
her cope with her MS better, use less pain
medication and become more mobile. She had
fewer flare-ups and scans even showed that
the disease had slowed its progression.[14]
She later set up a 'random acts of kindness'
organisation at *29gifts.org*.

....

DATE OR WEEK COMMENCING

....

DOMAIN 1 PLEASURE
Things that I enjoyed

....

....

....

....

....

....

....

DOMAIN 2 POSITIVE STROKES
Praise that I received

....

....

....

....

....

....

....

DOMAIN 3 LUCKY ME
Good fortune that I experienced

....

....

....

....

....

....

....

DOMAIN 4 ACHIEVEMENTS
Things that made me think 'well done me!'

....
....
....
....
....
....
....

DOMAIN 5 GRATITUDE
Blessings that I am grateful for

....
....
....
....
....
....
....

DOMAIN 6 RANDOM ACTS OF KINDNESS
Moments of kindness that I have performed

....
....
....
....
....
....
....

NOTES

....
....

....

DOMAIN 1 PLEASURE
Things that I enjoyed

....

....

....

....

....

....

....

DOMAIN 2 POSITIVE STROKES
Praise that I received

....

....

....

....

....

....

....

DOMAIN 3 LUCKY ME
Good fortune that I experienced

....

....

....

....

....

....

....

DOMAIN 4 ACHIEVEMENTS
Things that made me think 'well done me!'

....

....

....

....

....

....

....

DOMAIN 5 GRATITUDE
Blessings that I am grateful for

....

....

....

....

....

....

....

....

DOMAIN 6 RANDOM ACTS OF KINDNESS
Moments of kindness that I have performed

....

....

....

....

....

....

....

NOTES

....

....

....

Helping others can lift people out of a negative mood and sustain a positive mood.[15]

....

Going the Extra Mile

The Ten-Minute Programme should make a real difference to your life, but you can make things even better by doing just a few things more. The following suggestions scattered throughout the following pages in your journal are optional – but recommended.

Having Things to Look Forward To

Everyone should have things to look forward to. The Pleasure Principle was discussed in Domain 1 – the idea that we all need some pleasure in our lives. Similarly, we all need to know there is something good happening around the corner. It motivates us and keeps us going through the duller parts of our lives. It promises respite and fun or relaxation and calm – an oasis from the daily stresses and strains of everyday life.

Anticipation is the reason why we need things to look forward to; anticipation is part of the pleasure. Spontaneity is great but takes away the anticipation – and that can mean a reduction in the pleasure, since anticipation spreads the pleasure across a longer period.

Anticipation is rooted in the portion of the brain known as the cerebellum, which controls 'automatic, non-thinking' behaviour. Dopamine, that feel-good chemical, is released when we experience and expect enjoyable things. Anticipating positive events sustains the output of dopamine so that we have steadier levels of it rather than just sudden bursts when we actually do the pleasurable activity.[16]

....

DOMAIN 1 PLEASURE
Things that I enjoyed

....
....
....
....
....
....
....
....

DOMAIN 2 POSITIVE STROKES
Praise that I received

....
....
....
....
....
....
....
....

DOMAIN 3 LUCKY ME
Good fortune that I experienced

....
....
....
....
....
....
....
....

DOMAIN 4 ACHIEVEMENTS
Things that made me think 'well done me!'

....
....
....
....
....
....
....

DOMAIN 5 GRATITUDE
Blessings that I am grateful for

....
....
....
....
....
....
....

DOMAIN 6 RANDOM ACTS OF KINDNESS
Moments of kindness that I have performed

....
....
....
....
....
....
....

NOTES

....
....

....

DOMAIN 1 PLEASURE
Things that I enjoyed

....

....

....

....

....

....

....

DOMAIN 2 POSITIVE STROKES
Praise that I received

....

....

....

....

....

....

....

DOMAIN 3 LUCKY ME
Good fortune that I experienced

....

....

....

....

....

....

DOMAIN 4 ACHIEVEMENTS
Things that made me think 'well done me!'

....
....
....
....
....
....
....

DOMAIN 5 GRATITUDE
Blessings that I am grateful for

....
....
....
....
....
....
....

DOMAIN 6 RANDOM ACTS OF KINDNESS
Moments of kindness that I have performed

....
....
....
....
....
....
....

NOTES

....
....

....

DOMAIN 1 PLEASURE
Things that I enjoyed

....
....
....
....
....
....
....

DOMAIN 2 POSITIVE STROKES
Praise that I received

....
....
....
....
....
....
....

DOMAIN 3 LUCKY ME
Good fortune that I experienced

....
....
....
....
....
....

DOMAIN 4 ACHIEVEMENTS
Things that made me think 'well done me!'

....
....
....
....
....
....
....

DOMAIN 5 GRATITUDE
Blessings that I am grateful for

....
....
....
....
....
....
....

DOMAIN 6 RANDOM ACTS OF KINDNESS
Moments of kindness that I have performed

....
....
....
....
....
....
....

NOTES

....
....

Why Having Events (Rather than New Stuff) to Look Forward to Makes Us Happy

Cornell University psychological scientist Thomas Gilovich wanted to know if waiting for, or anticipating, an experience is more pleasurable and less negatively impactful than waiting for a new material possession (like a new laptop). He tested this by asking people to think about a purchase they intended to make in the very near future – either a life experience such as going to a concert or on holiday, or a tangible possession like a new phone or computer.

Importantly, the things they were looking forward to did not differ in cost, but they did differ in the effect they had on their state of mind. Looking forward to a concert or holiday was much more enjoyable than looking forward to owning a new laptop. And waiting for new experiences involved more excitement and less impatience than anticipating the arrival of new stuff, which involved more of a mix of impatience and excitement.[17]

So, to maximise the benefit of having something to look forward to, it is better to have those events as experiences rather than material goods.

The Art of Anticipation

Researchers suggest that there is an art to anticipation.
We can make anticipation into an active process, rather than
passive and, by doing so, we will benefit even more. We all
know that when we have a holiday or night out planned, for
example, the anticipation can be almost as enjoyable as the
event itself (sometimes, more so, if the event turns out to be a
disappointment). We can reap the benefits of this anticipation
even more by really savouring the planned event, by thinking
about it, immersing ourselves in it and by imagining it. For
example, if we are going on holiday, we can read travel guides,
learn some of the language and learn about the culture. Of
course, we might also shop for the trip and take pleasure in
buying the sun lotion and beachwear. All this can enhance the
anticipation and give us enjoyment long before the event.[18]

How can you achieve this sense of enhanced anticipation? In the
back of your journal (or elsewhere), keep a list of all the things
you have to look forward to over the next year. Keep revisiting
the list, to cross things off that have happened or add new things.
Also, revisiting will remind you of the good things to come and
will help build that all-important anticipation. Not much on
your list? Create events to plan in – arrange to meet friends for a
coffee, plan a trip out, a nice countryside hike or whatever floats
your boat.

....

DOMAIN 1 PLEASURE
Things that I enjoyed

....

....

....

....

....

....

....

DOMAIN 2 POSITIVE STROKES
Praise that I received

....

....

....

....

....

....

....

DOMAIN 3 LUCKY ME
Good fortune that I experienced

....

....

....

....

....

....

....

DOMAIN 4 ACHIEVEMENTS
Things that made me think 'well done me!'

....
....
....
....
....
....
....

DOMAIN 5 GRATITUDE
Blessings that I am grateful for

....
....
....
....
....
....

DOMAIN 6 RANDOM ACTS OF KINDNESS
Moments of kindness that I have performed

....
....
....
....
....
....
....

NOTES

....
....

....

DOMAIN 1 PLEASURE
Things that I enjoyed

....
....
....
....
....
....
....

DOMAIN 2 POSITIVE STROKES
Praise that I received

....
....
....
....
....
....
....

DOMAIN 3 LUCKY ME
Good fortune that I experienced

....
....
....
....
....
....
....

DOMAIN 4 ACHIEVEMENTS
Things that made me think 'well done me!'

....
....
....
....
....
....
....

DOMAIN 5 GRATITUDE
Blessings that I am grateful for

....
....
....
....
....
....
....

DOMAIN 6 RANDOM ACTS OF KINDNESS
Moments of kindness that I have performed

....
....
....
....
....
....
....

NOTES

....
....

Exercise Your Way to Happiness

Exercise is proven to makes us feel happier; in fact, the benefits to our mood of just twenty minutes of exercise can last a whopping twelve hours, according to researchers from the University of Vermont.[19] People who exercise a lot are happier and more satisfied with their lives.[20] And, although we are least likely to exercise when we are feeling low, it is when we are in a sad mood that exercise has the most benefit to our happiness levels – so one of the best things you can do when you are feeling down is force yourself to get up and go for a walk, a swim or a jog. In fact, although antidepressants cause the swiftest response in helping clinical depression, studies show that the effects of exercise last longer than those of antidepressants, and that patients who regularly exercised were less likely to relapse.[21]

The reason that exercise can have such a powerful effect on our mood is that it stimulates the production of endorphins and other feel-good chemicals in the body; this gives us the so-called 'runner's high' that you may have heard about. These neurochemicals, which give you that euphoric buzz, are produced in the brain's hypothalamus and pituitary gland and are structurally similar to the drug morphine, which is, of course, a powerful painkiller. Indeed, the purpose of endorphins is to combat feelings of pain and stress, but they also produce feelings of euphoria.

What's the Purpose of Endorphins?

When we start exercising, our brain recognises this as a moment of stress. As our heart rate increases in order to send more oxygen-rich blood to our muscles to give us the energy we need, the brain thinks we are either fighting the enemy or fleeing from it (the so-called 'flight or flight' response). To protect ourselves from this stress, our brains release endorphins (among other chemicals). These endorphins aim to minimise the discomfort of exercise, block the feeling of pain and produce that feeling of euphoria; this is so that if we really were fleeing a dangerous enemy (i.e. if we really were under stress), we wouldn't want to be distracted by pain and discomfort. That can come later when we are safe.

To reap the benefits, you don't even need to do excessive exercise; half an hour three times a week is enough to give you that mental health boost. Even a stroll around the block can have some benefit, although one study suggested that a thirty-minute walk is better for our mood than three walks lasting ten minutes.[22] Twenty minutes is suggested as the minimum to reap the benefits.

DATE OR WEEK COMMENCING

....

DOMAIN 1 PLEASURE
Things that I enjoyed

....
....
....
....
....
....
....

DOMAIN 2 POSITIVE STROKES
Praise that I received

....
....
....
....
....
....
....

DOMAIN 3 LUCKY ME
Good fortune that I experienced

....
....
....
....
....
....
....

DOMAIN 4 ACHIEVEMENTS
Things that made me think 'well done me!'

....
....
....
....
....
....
....

DOMAIN 5 GRATITUDE
Blessings that I am grateful for

....
....
....
....
....
....
....

DOMAIN 6 RANDOM ACTS OF KINDNESS
Moments of kindness that I have performed

....
....
....
....
....
....
....

NOTES

....
....

....

DOMAIN 1 PLEASURE
Things that I enjoyed

....
....
....
....
....
....
....

DOMAIN 2 POSITIVE STROKES
Praise that I received

....
....
....
....
....
....

DOMAIN 3 LUCKY ME
Good fortune that I experienced

....
....
....
....
....
....
....

DOMAIN 4 ACHIEVEMENTS
Things that made me think 'well done me!'

....
....
....
....
....
....
....

DOMAIN 5 GRATITUDE
Blessings that I am grateful for

....
....
....
....
....
....
....

DOMAIN 6 RANDOM ACTS OF KINDNESS
Moments of kindness that I have performed

....
....
....
....
....
....
....

NOTES

....
....

Laugh More

Laughing has proven benefits to our mood; it triggers positive emotions that are felt in the moment – it doesn't matter what went before or will come after, because all that matters is the present, and having fun right now. Having a sense of humour is well recognised as a coping mechanism for stress and negative life events and has been found to be associated with overall quality of life and psychological well-being.[23]

One study showed that bereaved people who engaged in laughter were more successful in emotionally distancing themselves from grief.[24] This is because it is hard to laugh and be sad at the same time, and laughter also triggers the release of those all-important feel-good endorphins. In fact, laughter can result in as much endorphin production as a good workout.[25] A study of ordinary (i.e. non-depressed or non-bereaved) participants found that students who used humour as a coping mechanism were more likely to be happy.[26]

Even forced laughter can be beneficial. According to the 'facial feedback' mechanism, if our brain perceives that we are smiling or laughing, even if we don't really feel like it, it will assume we must be having fun – i.e. 'My face is smiling so I must be happy ...' – and will produce the relevant chemicals that will actually bring the same benefits as a non-faked bout of laughter. Thus, merely smiling or artificially simulating laughing can be almost as beneficial as the real thing.

This is illustrated by a study conducted by psychologists in 2011 at the University of Cardiff in Wales, which found that people whose ability to frown was limited by cosmetic Botox injections were happier, on average, than people who could frown. This wasn't because the Botoxed people felt any more attractive (they checked that), but most likely because they were forced to have happier expressions on their faces.[27]

DATE OR WEEK COMMENCING

....

DOMAIN 1 PLEASURE
Things that I enjoyed

....

....

....

....

....

....

....

DOMAIN 2 POSITIVE STROKES
Praise that I received

....

....

....

....

....

....

....

DOMAIN 3 LUCKY ME
Good fortune that I experienced

....

....

....

....

....

....

....

DOMAIN 4 ACHIEVEMENTS
Things that made me think 'well done me!'

....

....

....

....

....

....

....

DOMAIN 5 GRATITUDE
Blessings that I am grateful for

....

....

....

....

....

....

....

DOMAIN 6 RANDOM ACTS OF KINDNESS
Moments of kindness that I have performed

....

....

....

....

....

....

....

NOTES

....

....

DATE OR WEEK COMMENCING

....

DOMAIN 1 PLEASURE
Things that I enjoyed

....:.........

....

....

....

....

....

....

DOMAIN 2 POSITIVE STROKES
Praise that I received

....

....

....

....

....

....

....

DOMAIN 3 LUCKY ME
Good fortune that I experienced

....

....

....

....

....

....

....

DOMAIN 4 ACHIEVEMENTS
Things that made me think 'well done me!'

....
....
....
....
....
....
....

DOMAIN 5 GRATITUDE
Blessings that I am grateful for

....
....
....
....
....
....
....

DOMAIN 6 RANDOM ACTS OF KINDNESS
Moments of kindness that I have performed

....
....
....
....
....
....
....

NOTES

....
....

DATE OR WEEK COMMENCING

....

DOMAIN 1 PLEASURE
Things that I enjoyed

....
....
....
....
....
....
....

DOMAIN 2 POSITIVE STROKES
Praise that I received

....
....
....
....
....
....
....

DOMAIN 3 LUCKY ME
Good fortune that I experienced

....
....
....
....
....
....

DOMAIN 4 ACHIEVEMENTS
Things that made me think 'well done me!'

....

....

....

....

....

....

....

DOMAIN 5 GRATITUDE
Blessings that I am grateful for

....

....

....

....

....

....

....

DOMAIN 6 RANDOM ACTS OF KINDNESS
Moments of kindness that I have performed

....

....

....

....

....

....

....

NOTES

....

....

More Reasons to Smile

Further evidence for the powerful, positive benefits of smiling and laughter is provided by an ingenious study reported in the journal *Psychological Science*, which involved researchers from the University of Kansas getting people to hold chopsticks in their mouths in such a way that they either produced neutral expressions or smiles. The chopstick technique ensured that the subjects were not aware that they were actually mimicking the muscle patterns of a smile. The researchers then gave all the participants a stressful activity and found that those who had arranged their faces into smiles showed faster recovery from the stress than those who hadn't. This suggests that smiling can help us cope with stress, even if we don't actually feel like smiling.[28]

This is the theory behind laughter yoga, which originated in 1995 by Dr Madan Kataria, a medical doctor from Mumbai, India. In laughter yoga (or laugher therapy) sessions, people simulate laughter with vigorous 'ha-has' and 'ho-hos' – these inevitably lead to genuine laughter that, in group sessions, is contagious.

The effect works the opposite way, too; people who frown during an unpleasant procedure report feeling more pain than those who do not, according to a study published in May 2008 in the *Journal of Pain*. Researchers applied heat to the forearms of 29 participants, who were asked to make either unhappy, neutral or relaxed faces during the procedure. Those who exhibited negative expressions reported being in more pain than those in the other two groups. It could well be, then, that in order to feel less pain, all we need to do is to smile.[29]

Exercise Your Way to Happiness

The National Institute for Health and Care Excellence (NICE) recommends that people with mild to moderate depression undertake around three one-hour sessions of exercise a week. Many GP surgeries across the country even prescribe exercise as a treatment for depression.[30]

A wealth of evidence shows that you will be able to achieve a noticeable and sustainable improvement in mood by aiming for thirty minutes' exercise three times a week as a starting point. This should be anything that gets your heart working. Keep track of this by writing an exercise diary and charting what you do each day. Look to make small changes to your lifestyle to incorporate exercise – e.g. park further away, use the stairs, get off the bus one stop earlier, etc.

DATE OR WEEK COMMENCING

....

DOMAIN 1 PLEASURE
Things that I enjoyed

....

....

....

....

....

....

....

....

DOMAIN 2 POSITIVE STROKES
Praise that I received

....

....

....

....

....

....

....

DOMAIN 3 LUCKY ME
Good fortune that I experienced

....

....

....

....

....

....

....

DOMAIN 4 ACHIEVEMENTS
Things that made me think 'well done me!'

....
....
....
....
....
....
....

DOMAIN 5 GRATITUDE
Blessings that I am grateful for

....
....
....
....
....
....
....

DOMAIN 6 RANDOM ACTS OF KINDNESS
Moments of kindness that I have performed

....
....
....
....
....
....
....

NOTES

....
....

DATE OR WEEK COMMENCING

....

DOMAIN 1 PLEASURE
Things that I enjoyed

....

....

....

....

....

....

....

DOMAIN 2 POSITIVE STROKES
Praise that I received

....

....

....

....

....

....

....

DOMAIN 3 LUCKY ME
Good fortune that I experienced

....

....

....

....

....

....

DOMAIN 4 ACHIEVEMENTS
Things that made me think 'well done me!'

....

....

....

....

....

....

....

DOMAIN 5 GRATITUDE
Blessings that I am grateful for

....

....

....

....

....

....

....

DOMAIN 6 RANDOM ACTS OF KINDNESS
Moments of kindness that I have performed

....

....

....

....

....

....

....

NOTES

....

....

Laugh and Others Will Laugh with You

Actually, most emotions are contagious – we, as social animals, are very good at copying people's moods, whether we intend to or not. It is thought to be intrinsically linked to social bonding; if others feel our emotions, we are more likely to bond with them. This phenomenon is called 'emotional contagion' and we are most likely to catch emotions from people we are close to.

The mechanism for emotional contagion is in the mimicking that we do of emotional displays. As we subconsciously mimic the fleeting emotional expressions of those around us, our brains interpret this as the genuine emotion. This 'ripple effect' of emotions can be very prevalent in groups, where emotional mood can spread quickly throughout a number of people (especially to those they feel close to). This is sometimes termed 'mood convergence' and research has shown this effect in teams of nurses, accountants and even professional cricket teams.[31]

Research also suggests that it is easier to catch negative emotions than positive ones, but it is the emotional intensity or level of energy involved that really makes the difference; emotion expressed in a high-energy fashion (e.g. a loud burst of laughter) tends to lead to greater contagion than those of lower energy (e.g. a smile).[32]

The laughter of others does seem to have a special impact on our brains. Researchers at University College London conducted a study where they played different sounds to volunteers and measured their brains' reactions to the sound. It was seen that responses were higher for positive sounds, such as laughing, and were much lower for negative sounds like screaming.[33] This suggests that humans are more primed to the sound of laughter as compared to negative sounds, which might go some way to explaining why we smile or even laugh when we see other people laughing. This is also why canned laughter during sitcoms is so effective at getting an audience to laugh.

Possibly the most famous case of contagious laughter was reported in 1962 – the so-called 'Tanganyika Laughter Epidemic'. Three girls studying in a boarding school in a village in Tanganyika (now Tanzania) began to laugh, and soon the laughter spread to the whole school. Symptoms lasted from a few hours to 16 days in those affected. Eventually, it affected about 95 of the 159 pupils and was so bad that school had to be closed, but even that didn't stop the spread of laughter; it is thought around 1,000 people, including those in local villages and other schools, were eventually affected.

DATE OR WEEK COMMENCING

....

DOMAIN 1 PLEASURE
Things that I enjoyed

....

....

....

....

....

....

....

DOMAIN 2 POSITIVE STROKES
Praise that I received

....

....

....

....

....

....

DOMAIN 3 LUCKY ME
Good fortune that I experienced

....

....

....

....

....

....

DOMAIN 4 ACHIEVEMENTS
Things that made me think 'well done me!'

....

....

....

....

....

....

....

DOMAIN 5 GRATITUDE
Blessings that I am grateful for

....

....

....

....

....

....

....

DOMAIN 6 RANDOM ACTS OF KINDNESS
Moments of kindness that I have performed

....

....

....

....

....

....

....

NOTES

....

....

....

DOMAIN 1 PLEASURE
Things that I enjoyed

....
....
....
....
....
....
....

DOMAIN 2 POSITIVE STROKES
Praise that I received

....
....
....
....
....
....
....

DOMAIN 3 LUCKY ME
Good fortune that I experienced

....
....
....
....
....
....
....

DOMAIN 4 ACHIEVEMENTS
Things that made me think 'well done me!'

....

....

....

....

....

....

DOMAIN 5 GRATITUDE
Blessings that I am grateful for

....

....

....

....

....

....

....

DOMAIN 6 RANDOM ACTS OF KINDNESS
Moments of kindness that I have performed

....

....

....

....

....

....

....

NOTES

....

....

....

Children Know How to Have Fun

Children tend to laugh around 300 times
a day, compared with a miserable 17 times
a day for adults.[34]

....

Why Do We Laugh?

Actually, scientists haven't been able to establish exactly what the mechanism in our brain is when we laugh. It is thought that the brain stem plays some role; some patients who have suffered strokes in this area have prolonged bouts of laughter that don't seem to have any real cause. It is also thought that some electrical activity is involved in a laugh. Scientists have shown that about half a second after we hear the punchline of a joke – but before we laugh – a wave of electricity travels through the whole cerebral cortex region of the brain, which suggests that almost all of these brain regions are involved in the laughter phenomenon.[35]

....

DOMAIN 1 PLEASURE
Things that I enjoyed

....

....

....

....

....

....

....

DOMAIN 2 POSITIVE STROKES
Praise that I received

....

....

....

....

....

....

....

DOMAIN 3 LUCKY ME
Good fortune that I experienced

....

....

....

....

....

....

....

DOMAIN 4 ACHIEVEMENTS
Things that made me think 'well done me!'

....

....

....

....

....

....

....

DOMAIN 5 GRATITUDE
Blessings that I am grateful for

....

....

....

....

....

....

....

DOMAIN 6 RANDOM ACTS OF KINDNESS
Moments of kindness that I have performed

....

....

....

....

....

....

....

NOTES

....

....

DATE OR WEEK COMMENCING

....

DOMAIN 1 PLEASURE
Things that I enjoyed

....
....
....
....
....
....
....

DOMAIN 2 POSITIVE STROKES
Praise that I received

....
....
....
....
....
....
....

DOMAIN 3 LUCKY ME
Good fortune that I experienced

....
....
....
....
....
....

DOMAIN 4 ACHIEVEMENTS
Things that made me think 'well done me!'

....

....

....

....

....

....

....

DOMAIN 5 GRATITUDE
Blessings that I am grateful for

....

....

....

....

....

....

....

DOMAIN 6 RANDOM ACTS OF KINDNESS
Moments of kindness that I have performed

....

....

....

....

....

....

....

NOTES

....

....

....

DOMAIN 1 PLEASURE
Things that I enjoyed

....
....
....
....
....
....
....

DOMAIN 2 POSITIVE STROKES
Praise that I received

....
....
....
....
....
....
....

DOMAIN 3 LUCKY ME
Good fortune that I experienced

....
....
....
....
....
....
....

DOMAIN 4 ACHIEVEMENTS
Things that made me think 'well done me!'

....
....
....
....
....
....
....

DOMAIN 5 GRATITUDE
Blessings that I am grateful for

....
....
....
....
....
....
....

DOMAIN 6 RANDOM ACTS OF KINDNESS
Moments of kindness that I have performed

....
....
....
....
....
....
....

NOTES

....
....

Simple Tips for a Smilier, Happier You

Smile – smiling is the beginning of laughter and, like laughter, it's contagious. When you look at someone or see something even mildly pleasing, practise smiling – you never know when this might develop into full-blown laughter.

Seek out humour – if you hear people laughing, ask them why. Look for opportunities to share jokes or to find something funny. Look for the humour yourself in situations.

Mix with fun, playful people – these are the sort of people who routinely find the humour in the mundane. These people laugh easily – both at themselves and at life.

Watch a funny programme or clip – comedians, *Friends* episodes – whatever makes you chortle. Incorporate a session of this every day as part of your laughter therapy.

Laugh at yourself – if something embarrassing happens to you, instead of seeing this as something to cringe about, use it as an opportunity to make people laugh. You will end up laughing about it, too.

Try some group therapy – join some like-minded souls at a laughter yoga/therapy workshop.

Reduce That Stress

Too much stress makes us miserable. It is hard to feel happy when we are regularly trying to do too much, fit too much in, don't have time to think, are constantly chasing our tail and always feel pressured. Indeed, a groundbreaking study in 2008 published in the *Journal of Happiness Studies* concluded what most of us intuitively know: that participants who perceived higher levels of stress reported being less happy than those with lower levels of stress.[36] Other studies have shown that chronic stress can contribute to depression.[37]

But why does stress make us unhappy? Chronic stress, especially, leads to raised cortisol as well as reduced serotonin and dopamine, which has been linked to depression. Stress, of course, is often linked to unhealthy lifestyles that can also contribute to unhappiness; when we are stressed, we tend to have less time or inclination to exercise, eat healthily, relax, laugh and have fun. All of which, of course, can make us unhappier.

DATE OR WEEK COMMENCING

....

DOMAIN 1 PLEASURE
Things that I enjoyed

....

....

....

....

....

....

....

DOMAIN 2 POSITIVE STROKES
Praise that I received

....

....

....

....

....

....

....

DOMAIN 3 LUCKY ME
Good fortune that I experienced

....

....

....

....

....

....

DOMAIN 4 ACHIEVEMENTS
Things that made me think 'well done me!'

....
....
....
....
....
....
....

DOMAIN 5 GRATITUDE
Blessings that I am grateful for

....
....
....
....
....
....
....

DOMAIN 6 RANDOM ACTS OF KINDNESS
Moments of kindness that I have performed

....
....
....
....
....
....
....

NOTES

....
....

....

DOMAIN 1 PLEASURE
Things that I enjoyed

....

....

....

....

....

....

....

....

....

DOMAIN 2 POSITIVE STROKES
Praise that I received

....

....

....

....

....

....

....

DOMAIN 3 LUCKY ME
Good fortune that I experienced

....

....

....

....

....

....

....

DOMAIN 4 ACHIEVEMENTS
Things that made me think 'well done me!'

....

....

....

....

....

....

....

DOMAIN 5 GRATITUDE
Blessings that I am grateful for

....

....

....

....

....

....

....

DOMAIN 6 RANDOM ACTS OF KINDNESS
Moments of kindness that I have performed

....

....

....

....

....

....

....

NOTES

....

....

Why Modern Technology
Makes Us Stressed and Unhappy

We are immersed in technology these days. From the moment we wake to when our heads finally hit the pillow – and sometimes beyond – we are constantly bombarded with images, sounds, novelty and stimulation. Whether it be Facebook, Twitter, Instagram, Pinterest, email, Google, newsfeeds or blogs, we live in a world of constant connectivity. Most of us have smartphones that are perpetually twitching, buzzing, pinging and vibrating with messages and people trying to reach us.

The problem with this rapid and constantly changing flow of communication and information is that it can be cognitively taxing – in other words, it can overwhelm us as we try to keep up with everyone and everything. Compared with our ancestors, our pace of life is incredibly fast and this can leave us in a bewildered state of feeling overloaded. Trying to keep up with it all can cause pressure and never switching off leaves us stressed and exhausted.

The stress of all this connectivity isn't even necessarily worth it – it's not like all this makes us happier. In fact, recent studies suggest that use of social media makes us less happy, not more. A recent survey found as many as one in five people say they feel depressed as a result of using social media.[38] As one commentator put it; 'The stress of constantly monitoring our statuses and endlessly documenting every aspect of our lives via networks like Facebook, Snapchat and Instagram is taking its toll.'[39]

....

DOMAIN 1 PLEASURE
Things that I enjoyed

....
....
....
....
....
....
....
....

DOMAIN 2 POSITIVE STROKES
Praise that I received

....
....
....
....
....
....
....

DOMAIN 3 LUCKY ME
Good fortune that I experienced

....
....
....
....
....
....

DOMAIN 4 ACHIEVEMENTS
Things that made me think 'well done me!'

....

....

....

....

....

....

....

DOMAIN 5 GRATITUDE
Blessings that I am grateful for

....

....

....

....

....

....

....

DOMAIN 6 RANDOM ACTS OF KINDNESS
Moments of kindness that I have performed

....

....

....

....

....

....

....

NOTES

....

....

DATE OR WEEK COMMENCING

....

DOMAIN 1 PLEASURE
Things that I enjoyed

....

....

....

....

....

....

....

DOMAIN 2 POSITIVE STROKES
Praise that I received

....

....

....

....

....

....

....

DOMAIN 3 LUCKY ME
Good fortune that I experienced

....

....

....

....

....

....

DOMAIN 4 ACHIEVEMENTS
Things that made me think 'well done me!'

....
....
....
....
....
....
....

DOMAIN 5 GRATITUDE
Blessings that I am grateful for

....
....
....
....
....
....
....

DOMAIN 6 RANDOM ACTS OF KINDNESS
Moments of kindness that I have performed

....
....
....
....
....
....
....

NOTES

....
....

Top Tips for Managing Your Busy Lifestyle

Try to do less. Learn to say no (consider books on assertiveness or training courses) or think about why you feel the need to take so much on; sometimes it is about feeling valued or useful more than anything. Address those needs so you are able to manage your commitments better.

Cut corners where possible. Getting a cleaner once a week or takeaways/supermarket meals occasionally will cost money but the benefits to your mental health and happiness might be worth it.

Learn relaxation techniques. You can download apps that teach you skills such as Progressive Muscle Relaxation. Or take up yoga, meditation or gardening – whatever works for you.

Switch off to switch on. Have a digital detox holiday, day or even hour a week. Being disconnected might seem daunting at first, but it will reap dividends. Switching off for an hour or two in the evening will also stop you zoning out and wasting time on social media, etc.

Have respite. Maybe you have a really stressful job but that doesn't mean you can't have respite from it at times. Take regular breaks where you force yourself to do something completely different – swim, run, paint, knit. Make use of the weekends and holidays (make sure you use up all of your annual leave – and leave that work phone behind!).

Keep a stress journal. Note your triggers and causes so you can identify patterns and common themes. This will help you start to tackle them and replace unhealthy coping mechanisms (e.g. smoking, alcohol) for healthier ones (a balanced diet, exercise).

DATE OR WEEK COMMENCING

....

DOMAIN 1 PLEASURE
Things that I enjoyed

....
....
....
....
....
....

DOMAIN 2 POSITIVE STROKES
Praise that I received

....
....
....
....
....
....

DOMAIN 3 LUCKY ME
Good fortune that I experienced

....
....
....
....
....
....

DOMAIN 4 ACHIEVEMENTS
Things that made me think 'well done me!'

....
....
....
....
....
....
....

DOMAIN 5 GRATITUDE
Blessings that I am grateful for

....
....
....
....
....
....
....

DOMAIN 6 RANDOM ACTS OF KINDNESS
Moments of kindness that I have performed

....
....
....
....
....
....
....

NOTES

....
....

DATE OR WEEK COMMENCING

....

DOMAIN 1 PLEASURE
Things that I enjoyed

....

....

....

....

....

....

....

DOMAIN 2 POSITIVE STROKES
Praise that I received

....

....

....

....

....

....

....

DOMAIN 3 LUCKY ME
Good fortune that I experienced

....

....

....

....

....

....

....

DOMAIN 4 ACHIEVEMENTS
Things that made me think 'well done me!'

....

....

....

....

....

....

....

DOMAIN 5 GRATITUDE
Blessings that I am grateful for

....

....

....

....

....

....

....

DOMAIN 6 RANDOM ACTS OF KINDNESS
Moments of kindness that I have performed

....

....

....

....

....

....

....

NOTES

....

....

DATE OR WEEK COMMENCING

....

DOMAIN 1 PLEASURE
Things that I enjoyed

....
....
....
....
....
....
....
....

DOMAIN 2 POSITIVE STROKES
Praise that I received

....
....
....
....
....
....
....
....

DOMAIN 3 LUCKY ME
Good fortune that I experienced

....
....
....
....
....
....
....

DOMAIN 4 ACHIEVEMENTS
Things that made me think 'well done me!'

....

....

....

....

....

....

....

DOMAIN 5 GRATITUDE
Blessings that I am grateful for

....

....

....

....

....

....

DOMAIN 6 RANDOM ACTS OF KINDNESS
Moments of kindness that I have performed

....

....

....

....

....

....

....

NOTES

....

....

Gratitude v Appreciation
(and Other Concepts)

Gratitude is easy to confuse with other related conditions. For example, indebtedness is a much more contained and restricted obligation (or perceived obligation) towards a benefactor, which involves some sort of payback for a favour or act of kindness. Unlike gratitude, indebtedness can lead the beneficiary to feel uncomfortable in the presence of the benefactor, and may even lead to resentment.

Appreciation is very similar to gratitude but with subtle differences. Gratitude is more about being thankful for something, whereas appreciation is more about enjoyment. We are grateful for food but appreciate the taste and flavours. We need to appreciate things in order to be grateful for them.

In the context of the Ten-Minute Programme, the distinction between gratitude and appreciation is not important.

....

Luck and Extroversion

Extrovert people are more likely to be 'lucky' – because they have a bigger network of friends and acquaintances to help them out. They are more likely to have a fortuitous encounter if they can strike up a conversation in the supermarket queue.[40]

....

DATE OR WEEK COMMENCING

....

DOMAIN 1 PLEASURE
Things that I enjoyed

....
....
....
....
....
....
....

DOMAIN 2 POSITIVE STROKES
Praise that I received

....
....
....
....
....
....
....

DOMAIN 3 LUCKY ME
Good fortune that I experienced

....
....
....
....
....
....
....

DOMAIN 4 ACHIEVEMENTS
Things that made me think 'well done me!'

....

....

....

....

....

....

....

DOMAIN 5 GRATITUDE
Blessings that I am grateful for

....

....

....

....

....

....

....

DOMAIN 6 RANDOM ACTS OF KINDNESS
Moments of kindness that I have performed

....

....

....

....

....

....

....

NOTES

....

....

DATE OR WEEK COMMENCING

....

DOMAIN 1 PLEASURE
Things that I enjoyed

....
....
....
....
....
....
....

DOMAIN 2 POSITIVE STROKES
Praise that I received

....
....
....
....
....
....
....

DOMAIN 3 LUCKY ME
Good fortune that I experienced

....
....
....
....
....
....
....

DOMAIN 4 ACHIEVEMENTS
Things that made me think 'well done me!'

....
....
....
....
....
....
....

DOMAIN 5 GRATITUDE
Blessings that I am grateful for

....
....
....
....
....
....
....

DOMAIN 6 RANDOM ACTS OF KINDNESS
Moments of kindness that I have performed

....
....
....
....
....
....
....

NOTES

....
....

....

DOMAIN 1 PLEASURE
Things that I enjoyed

....
....
....
....
....
....
....
....

DOMAIN 2 POSITIVE STROKES
Praise that I received

....
....
....
....
....
....
....
....

DOMAIN 3 LUCKY ME
Good fortune that I experienced

....
....
....
....
....
....
....

DOMAIN 4 ACHIEVEMENTS
Things that made me think 'well done me!'

....
....
....
....
....
....
....

DOMAIN 5 GRATITUDE
Blessings that I am grateful for

....
....
....
....
....
....
....

DOMAIN 6 RANDOM ACTS OF KINDNESS
Moments of kindness that I have performed

....
....
....
....
....
....
....

NOTES

....
....

References and Bibliography

Introduction – It's Sad to be Sad

1   Hertel P., 'Memory for Emotional and Non-Emotional Events in Depression: A Question of Habit?' (2004). In D. Reisberg and P. Hertel (Eds.), *Memory and Emotion*. New York: Oxford University Press, 186–216

2   https://www.theatlantic.com/magazine/archive/2009/06/what-makes-us-happy/307439/2.

3   https://www.weforum.org/agenda/2016/09/the-link-between-being-unhappy-at-work-and-your-health

4   Kross E., Verduyn P., Demiralp E., Park J., Lee D.S., Lin N., et al. *Facebook Use Predicts Declines in Subjective Well-Being in Young Adults* (2013). PLoS ONE 8(8): e69841. https://doi.org/10.1371/journal.pone.0069841

5   http://www.stylist.co.uk/life/10-things-that-are-scientifically-proven-to-make-you-unhappy

6   http://www.marketwatch.com/story/americans-less-happy-now-than-in-2007-says-latest-world-happiness-report-2016-03-17; see also Helliwell, J., Layard, R., & Sachs, J., *World Happiness Report* 2017, New York: Sustainable Development Solutions Network (2017)

7   http://observer.com/2015/07/why-keeping-a-daily-journal-could-change-your-life/

8   ibid.

9   http://www.apa.org/monitor/jun02/writing.aspx

Domain 1 – Pleasure

1   Mann S., *The Science of Boredom: the Upside (and Downside) of Downtime*, London: Little, Brown (2017)

2   http://healthland.time.com/2011/08/26/mind-reading-how-pleasure-works/

3   Katherine Harmon, 'Addicted to Fat: Overeating May Alter the Brain as Much as Hard Drugs', *Scientific American*, 28 March 2010; http://www.scientificamerican.com/article/addicted-to-fat-eating/

4   ibid.

5   http://www.huffingtonpost.com/margaret-paul-phd/the-difference-between-happiness-and-pleasure_b_7053946.html

6   http://metro.co.uk/2013/08/08/purpose-or-pleasure-why-the-pursuit-of-happiness-matters-to-our-genes-3915388/

Domain 2 – Positive Strokes

1   http://www.positivepanicattacks.com/gamespeopleplayericbernetransactionalanalysisstrokes.html

2   https://www.psychologytoday.com/blog/the-squeaky-wheel/201308/why-some-people-hate-receiving-compliments

3   http://www.dailymail.co.uk/sciencetech/article-2947983/Always-Facebook-probably-insecure-People-concerned-rejection-thrive-comments-likes-study-claims.html

Domain 3 – Lucky Me

1   http://www.telegraph.co.uk/technology/3304496/Be-lucky-its-an-easy-skill-to-learn.html

2   ibid.

3   https://www.psychologytoday.com/articles/201005/make-your-own-luck

4   https://www.theguardian.com/lifeandstyle/2016/jul/25/psychology-donald-trump-win-luck-superstition

5   ibid.

6 ibid.

7 ibid.

8 https://www.scientificamerican.com/article/as-luck-would-have-it/

9 ibid.

Domain 4 – Achievements

1 https://www.forbes.com/sites/williamarruda/2013/10/22/the-one-thing-successful-people-do-every-day/#2abdb46f7c6a

2 https://www.psychologytoday.com/articles/199207/the-secrets-happiness

3 https://www.forbes.com/sites/williamarruda/2013/10/22/the-one-thing-successful-people-do-every-day/#2abdb46f7c6a

4 https://hbr.org/2011/05/the-power-of-small-wins

5 https://hbr.org/2011/05/small-wins-and-feeling-good

Domain 5 – Gratitude

1 https://www.psychologytoday.com/blog/prefrontal-nudity/201211/the-grateful-brain

2 http://happierhuman.com/benefits-of-gratitude/

3 ibid.

4 https://www.psychologytoday.com/blog/prefrontal-nudity/201211/the-grateful-brain

5 ibid.

6 https://www.psychologytoday.com/blog/.../7-scientifically-proven-benefits-gratitude

7 ibid.

8 ibid.

9 ibid.

10 http://happierhuman.com/benefits-of-gratitude/

11 https://www.psychologytoday.com/blog/.../7-scientifically-proven-benefits-gratitude

12 ibid.

13 Prathik Kini, Joel Wong, Sydney McInnis, Nicole Gabana, Joshua W. Brown, 'The effects of gratitude expression on neural activity', *NeuroImage*, Volume 128, March 2016: 1–10

14 http://journal.frontiersin.org/article/10.3389/fpsyg.2015.01491/full

Domain 6 – Random Acts of Kindness

1 Keiko Otake, Satoshi Shimai, Junko Tanaka-Matsumi, Kanako Otsui, Barbara L. Fredrickson, 'Happy people become happier through kindness: a counting kindnesses intervention' (2006), *J Happiness Stud*, Sep; 7(3): 361–375

2 http://www.denverpost.com/business/ci_23833404/deboskey-giving-helps-others-but-also-helps-giver

3 Casiday R., Kinsman E., Fisher C., Bambra C.: 'Volunteering and health: what impact does it really have?' *Final Report to Volunteering England*, London, UK: Volunteering England (2008)

4 Caroline E. Jenkinson, Andy P. Dickens, Kerry Jones, Jo Thompson-Coon, Rod S. Taylor, Morwenna Rogers, Clare L. Bambra, Iain Lang and Suzanne H. Richards, 'Is volunteering a public health intervention? A systematic review and meta-analysis of the health and survival of volunteers', *BMC Public Health* (2013) 13: 773

5 http://www.nytimes.com/2009/12/01/health/01well.html

6 http://www.huffingtonpost.com/david-r-hamilton-phd/kindness-benefits_b_869537.html

7 ibid.

8 Paul Arnstein, Michelle Vidal, Carol Wells-Federman, Betty Morgan, Margaret Caudill, 'From chronic pain patient to peer: Benefits and risks of volunteering', *Pain Management Nursing*, Volume 3, Issue 3, September 2002: 94–103

9 Doug Oman, Carl E. Thoresen, Kay McMahon, 'Volunteerism and Mortality among the Community-dwelling Elderly', *J Health Psychol*, May 1999, vol. 4 no. 3: 301–316

10 http://www.webmd.com/balance/features/science-good-deeds?page=2

11 Gail H. Ironson, MD, PhD and H'sien Hayward, BA, 'Do Positive Psychosocial Factors Predict Disease Progression in HIV-1? A Review of the Evidence', *Psychosom Med*, Jun 2008; 70(5): 546–554

12 http://www.webmd.com/balance/features/science-good-deeds?page=2

13 http://www.denverpost.com/business/ci_23833404/deboskey-giving-helps-others-but-also-helps-giver

The Journal

1 http://greatergood.berkeley.edu/article/item/four_ways_sadness_may_be_good_for_you

2 https://www.theguardian.com/money/2016/jan/07/can-money-buy-happiness

3 Daniel Kahneman and Angus Deaton, 'High income improves evaluation of life but not emotional well-being', 2010 PNAS, vol. 107, no. 38: 16489–16493

4 https://psychcentral.com/lib/what-makes-us-happy/

5 http://blog.deliveringhappiness.com/blog/overworking-makes-us-unhappy-but-why

6   Seligman, Martin E. P., *Flourish: A Visionary New Understanding of Happiness and Well-being*, New York: Simon and Schuster. p. 16. ISBN 9781439190760. Retrieved 1 April 2017

7   https://www.theatlantic.com/magazine/archive/2009/06/what-makes-us-happy/307439/

8   https://www.scientificamerican.com/article/as-luck-would-have-it/

9   Dulin, Patrick, Hill, Robert D., Anderson, Jay, Rasmussen, Dwight, 'Altruism as a predictor of life satisfaction in a sample of low-income older adult service providers', *Journal of Mental Health and Ageing*, Vol 7(3): 349–360 (2001)

10 Sonja Lyubomirsky, Kennon M. Sheldon, David Schkade, 'Pursuing Happiness: The Architecture of Sustainable Change', *Review of General Psychology*, Vol. 9, No. 2: 111–131 (2005)

11 http://news.wisc.edu/virtue-rewarded-helping-others-at-work-makes-people-happier/

12 Layous K., Nelson S. K., Oberle E., Schonert-Reichl K. A., Lyubomirsky S., 'Kindness Counts: Prompting Prosocial Behavior in Preadolescents Boosts Peer Acceptance and Well-Being', PLoS ONE7 (12): e51380 (2012). https://doi.org/10.1371/journal.pone.0051380

13 http://www.thespec.com/living-story/2099542-doing-good-deeds-boosts-happiness-self-esteem-study-shows/

14 http://www.nytimes.com/2009/12/01/health/01well.html

15 Barasch A., Levine E. E. , Berman J. Z. , Small D. A., 'Selfish or selfless? On the signal value of emotion in altruistic behavior', *J Pers Soc Psychol*, Sep;107(3): 393–413 (2014)

16 https://unbounce.com/conversion-rate-optimization/psychology-of-anticipation-conversion-rates/

17 http://www.huffingtonpost.com/wray-herbert/anticipation-the-psycholo_b_5588654.html

18 https://www.nytimes.com/2014/05/11/travel/what-a-great-trip-and-im-not-even-there-yet.html?_r=0

19 http://www.happify.com/hd/exercise-and-happiness-infographic/

20 ibid.

21 http://totalwellnessmagazine.org/body/the-science-behind-happiness-and-exercise

22 http://www.happify.com/hd/exercise-and-happiness-infographic/

23 Folkman S., Moskowitz J. T., 'Positive emotions and the other side of coping', *American Psychologist*, 2000; 55: 647–654

24 Hill R. D., *Positive Aging*, New York: W. W. Norton; 2005

25 http://www.beliefnet.com/wellness/health/laughter-is-the-new-old-secret-to-happiness.aspx

26 https://www.psychologytoday.com/articles/199607/happily-ever-laughter

27 Mann S., *Emotion: All That Matters*, London: Hodder and Stoughton, 2014

28 ibid.

29 ibid.

30 http://www.huffingtonpost.co.uk/entry/the-link-between-exercise-and-happiness_uk_573d97bae4b058ab71e656f3

31 ibid.

32 ibid.

33 https://www.scienceabc.com/humans/why-is-laughter-so-contagious.html

34 https://www.psychologytoday.com/articles/199607/happily-ever-laughter

35 ibid.

36 Holly H. Schiffrin, S. Katherine Nelson, 'Stressed and Happy? Investigating the Relationship Between Happiness and Perceived Stress', *Journal of Happiness Studies*, Volume 11, Issue 1: 33–39, March 2010

37 https://www.psychologytoday.com/blog/evolutionary-psychiatry/201103/how-stress-makes-you-sick-and-sad

38 http://www.independent.co.uk/voices/social-media-is-making-us-depressed-lets-learn-to-turn-it-off-a6974526.html

39 ibid.

40 https://www.psychologytoday.com/articles/201005/make-your-own-luck